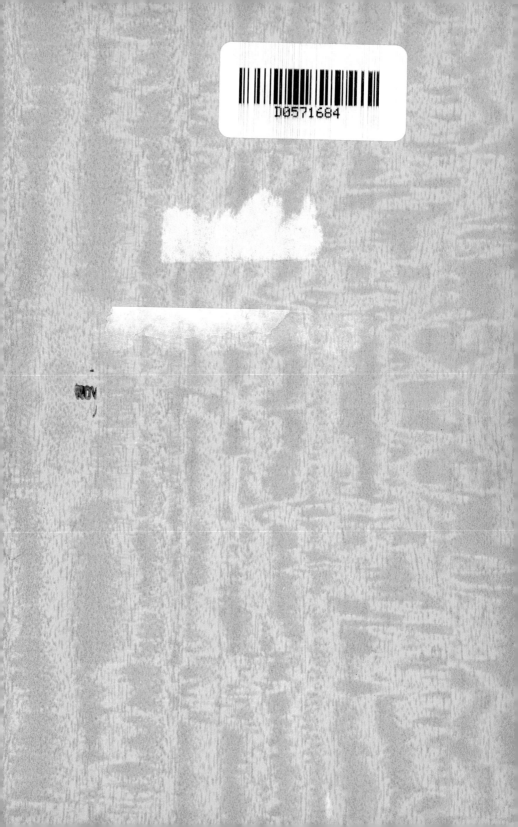

INTRODUCTION

TO DESIGN

MORRIS ASIMOW

Professor of Engineering
University of California, Los Angeles

PRENTICE-HALL, INC., Englewood Cliffs, N. J./1962

PRENTICE-HALL SERIES IN ENGINEERING DESIGN

JAMES B. RESWICK, *editor*

FUNDAMENTALS OF ENGINEERING DESIGN

Library of Congress Catalog Card Number 62–10550

Printed in the United States of America

47983C

FOREWORD

Design is the essential purpose of engineering. It begins with the recognition of a need and the conception of an idea to meet this need. It proceeds with the definition of the problem, continues through a program of directed research and development, and leads to the construction and evaluation of a prototype. It concludes with the effective multiplication and distribution of a product or system so that the original need may be met wherever it exists.

Introduction to Design is the first text in a series of books which will constitute a comprehensive reference source for instructors and students in engineering courses concerned with design, as well as practicing engineers. The series is divided into two parts. "Fundamentals of Engineering Design" contains those books which relate to the philosophy and discipline of design; while "Studies in Engineering Design" includes selected areas and specific cases wherein the philosophy and discipline of design is exemplified.

It is the hope of the authors that those concerned with developing new teaching programs in engineering design will find this series a source from which they may choose selected references which emphasize those aspects of design on which they may build their courses.

J. B. RESWICK

ENGINEERING DESIGN SERIES—BOOKS NOW IN PREPARATION

Fundamentals of Engineering Design

Introduction to Design–*Asimow*

Reliability in Engineering Design–
  Reethof and Queen

Design with Computers–*Curry*

Communication in Engineering Design–
  Rosenstein, Rathbone and Schneerer

Creativity in Engineering Design–
  Alger and Hayes

Studies in Engineering Design

Shock and Vibration–*Crede*

Modern Gear Dynamics–*Richardson*

Kinematics–*Freudenstein*

Appliance Design–*Woodson*

CONTENTS

An Example of Linear Programming in Design · Method of Steepest Descent · An Application of the Method of Steepest Descent · Test for a True Extreme · Optimization under Functional Constraints · An Application of the Method of Lagrangian Multipliers · The Newton-Raphson Approximation Method · An Example Involving Simultaneous Nonlinear Equations in Optimization · Optimizing under Regional Constraints.

A PHILOSOPHY

OF ENGINEERING DESIGN

DEFINITION OF ENGINEERING DESIGN

Engineering design is a purposeful activity directed toward the goal of fulfilling human needs, particularly those which can be met by the technological factors of our culture. The satisfaction of these needs is not peculiar to engineering design; it is common to much of human activity. Earning a living by serving the requirements of others is one of the chief characteristics of the modern social environment.

A designer does not usually produce the goods or services which immediately satisfy a consumer's needs. Rather, he produces the model which is used as a template for replicating the particular good or service as many times as is required. A design may be of a pattern on wall paper or of a garment in the world of fashion. If the producer believes that a sufficient number of customers will be satisfied by replicas, then production of the item or service may follow. In the course of production an error made by the producer in fabricating any one replica may lead to a rejection; but an error in design, repeated in all replicas, may lead to an economic misadventure of serious proportions. The designer's responsibility is therefore large.

As a profession, Engineering is largely concerned with design. What distinguishes the objects of engineering design from those of other design activities is the extent to which technological factors must contribute to their achievement. Every design activity that finally leads to a physical embodiment of the designer's conception must perforce make some use of technical factors. The key is the level of sophistication required in the manipulation and application of these factors and the extent to which a well-developed understanding of the underlying physical phenomena is necessary. Thus the sculptor, who produces his design in marble or bronze, is principally concerned with the aesthetic factors of form, shape, and texture. He is most likely aware of the technical behavior of his medium; but this is not his primary concern. It is sufficient for him to know as much about the technical factors which impinge on his design as would a highly skilled craftsman. To generalize, if a design can be accomplished properly with a simple technology, or with one that can be reduced to a routine that can be learned at the craftsman's level, then engineering design is not required. Engineering design *is* involved when the appropriate technology is complex and its application not obvious, and when the prediction and optimization of the outcome requires analytical procedures. Engineering design almost always requires a synthesis of technical, human, and economic factors; and it requires the consideration of social, political, and other factors whenever they are relevant.

DESIGN BY EVOLUTION

The feature that seems most characteristic of our times is the rapid pace of technological development. Scientific discoveries, multiplying in frequency, become available for technological exploitation. Society, which in the past had tended to abhor rapid change, has become receptive of and eager, and at times even impatient, for new feats of engineering design.

In the past, designs tended to evolve over long spans of time. Devices or technical systems changed gradually as time went on, each change making a small improvement on the preceding model. The leisurely pace of technological change reduced the risk of making major errors. The circumstances rarely demanded, and consequently seldom elicited, the utmost skill and analytical capabilities of the designer. This was "design by evolution"; the technical risks were small, and the stakes were proportionally small.

It is true that competition has long presented a stern and relentless challenge, but the contest, occurring on the commercial plane, was primarily waged in the market place. The designer was shielded by the salesman. Today the range of competitive action has widened. The struggle appears not only in the market place, but in the design office and the development laboratory as well. The challenge has moved to the technological plane, where the gradual and unhurried improvement of a product is now less likely to meet the demands of competition. Present circumstances require bolder, faster improvements. Consequently, the technical risks which engineering designers must face today are very great, as are the stakes–so large that they transcend the bounds of private interest and sometimes involve the entire national economy.

DESIGN BY INNOVATION

More frequently now than ever in the past, products are designed *de novo*. Following a scientific discovery, a new body of technical knowledge develops rapidly, the proper use of which may dictate an almost complete break with past practice. A new design is projected, based on ideas hitherto untried. The outcomes are shrouded in the obscurity of the future and blurred by the complexity of the technology. The risk of technical errors is immense. Every skill which the designer or the design team can muster in analysis and synthesis is scarcely enough.

The analytical tools which derive from the engineering sciences relating to fluid flow, heat transfer, electrical phenomena, etc. are well developed

2

and need no elaboration here; but besides dealing with these physical phenomena, the designer encounters a host of problems which are peculiar to the process of design. They arise from the need of developing, organizing, and evaluating information almost always in the face of uncertainty, from the necessity of taking into account the complicated interactions of components, from the constant requirement to make predictions in terms of design criteria, and from the need to work always within the constraints of an economic framework. We will speak of the analytical techniques which cope with these problems as the general methods and tools of design as distinguished from the specific tools which arise from the engineering sciences. It will be the general methods and tools of design, not the specific tools, that will be our concern in this text.

PHILOSOPHY AND DISCIPLINE

Philosophy may seem like a forbidding word to an engineer; but it simply means, in its literal sense, a love of wisdom. More specifically, a philosophy implies wisdom that has been organized to form a usable intellectual structure. It is a body of principles and general concepts which underly a given branch of learning, a major discipline, a religious system, or any other important human activity; and it includes the application of these principles in the domain of their relevance. Thus we can speak of a philosophy of history, or of business, or of Christianity. Philosophy has another meaning: it is a consistent and integrated personal attitude toward life, or reality, or certain phases of them. Thus, for example, it could be one's attitude towards his profession, especially if this attitude is expressed in beliefs or principles of conduct.

A philosophy does not spell out the detailed action one should take in specific instances; rather, it deals with underlying principles, concepts, and general methods which are relevant to whole classes of problems. The broad principles, the concepts, and the general methods of the philosophy lead to the development of theories, laws, and rules and to detailed methods of applying them. The latter is the discipline of design; it derives from philosophy, and it deals with recognizable categories of problems rather than with the general or the very specific.

Whereas a philosophy forms an intellectual superstructure or overall strategy which molds and guides the development of discipline, discipline provides an intermediate intellectual structure or strategy which molds and guides the attack on categories of problems. The practitioner, when dealing with an immediate and particular problem, must develop from his knowledge of discipline a specific attack or tactic which resolves that problem.

PHILOSOPHY OF ENGINEERING DESIGN

To develop a philosophy of engineering design we must seek out those principles and concepts that are of the greatest generality, consistent with

3

usefulness, and that can lead to a discipline of design. We must formulate a method whereby the discipline of design is applied in the most general sense. We will need also to establish a third element to take care of the evaluative function by setting forth a general critique that provides a way of measuring the validity and value of results in specific application.

The principles and concepts on which we must rely stem from the collective experiences of mankind. They represent, in an empirical sense, what we believe to be true. As a rule, we cannot prove by means of logic that any particular principle is true; we can only support our belief in its truth on the empirical evidence of experience. Hence it is inevitable that the choice of principles, and their formulation, will be colored and biased by our personal experiences and idiosyncrasies. For this reason there cannot be *one* philosophy of engineering design, any more than there can be *one* philosophy of history, or *one* philosophy of science. In architecture, for example, there have been in the past, as there are at the present time, many schools of thought, each representing a different philosophy with its adherents.

Although the choice and formulation of the principles that underlie a philosophy are subject to the vagaries of the individuals who construct it, the principles themselves must nonetheless be bound by the rules of logic. This must be so if we wish to exert the power of logic in applying them to the situations which are subordinate to the philosophy. The principles must, therefore, form a consistent set, so that one does not contradict another. They must be capable of expansion by logical combination and extension to form a larger body of derived principles on which discipline may find a secure foundation.

A philosophy that does not lead to action is sterile; it becomes an exercise without consequence. It must embody, if it is to be useful, a methodology whereby the principles can be applied in a disciplined way. This operational aspect is the chief burden of discipline; it involves the procedural, logical, and quantitative techniques that occupy much of the remaining text.

The origin of the philosophy is empirical, but its test is pragmatic. The solutions to which it leads must be good in the sense that they are useful. But good is a relative term that needs a specific definition especially tailored for each particular situation; its value needs to be measured in a way that is peculiar to each situation. Therefore, the philosophy must include an evaluative scheme which guides and enables the formulation of specific criteria of goodness. This evaluative element is essentially a feedback mechanism which serves to indicate how well the principles have been applied in the particular instance and to reveal shortcomings so that an improved application of the principles can be made.

In the view which is set forth here, a philosophy of engineering design comprises three major parts, namely, a set of consistent principles and their logical derivatives, an operational discipline which leads to action, and finally a critical feedback apparatus which measures the advantages,

4

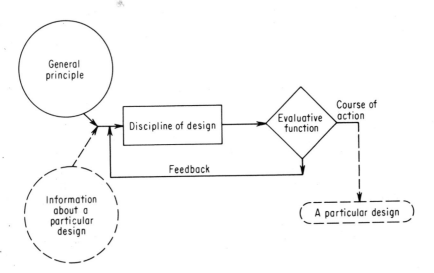

FIG. 1.1 Philosophy of Design. The feedback becomes operable when a solution is judged to be inadequate and requires improvement. The dotted elements represent a particular application.

detects the shortcomings, and illuminates the directions of improvement. These ideas, abbreviated and perhaps oversimplified, are diagrammed in Figure 1.1.

We shall conclude this chapter with a listing of the principles on which subsequent discussions will rest. Other concepts and ideas which can be informally derived from this set are advanced as needed. The word *design*, wherever it appears in the following, will mean engineering design. The list is not intended to be a rigid set of formal postulates.

(1) *Need.* Design must be a response to individual or social needs which can be satisfied by the technological factors of culture.

(2) *Physical Realizability.* The object of a design is material good or service which must be physically realizable.

(3) *Economic Worthwhileness.* The good or service, described by a design, must have a utility to the consumer that equals or exceeds the sum of the proper costs of making it available to him.

(4) *Financial Feasibility.* The operations of designing, producing, and distributing the good must be financially supportable.

(5) *Optimality.* The choice of a design concept must be optimal among the available alternatives; the selection of a manifestation of the chosen design concept must be optimal among all permissible manifestations.

(6) *Design Criterion.* Optimality must be established relative to a design criterion which represents the designer's compromise among possibly conflicting value judgments that include those of the consumer, the producer, the distributor, and his own.

(7) *Morphology.* Design is a progression from the abstract to the concrete. (This gives a vertical structure to a design project.)

(8) *Design Process.* Design is an iterative problem-solving process. (This gives a horizontal structure to each design step.)

(9) *Subproblems.* In attending to the solution of a design problem, there is uncovered a substratum of subproblems; the solution of the original problem is dependent on the solution of the subproblem.

(10) *Reduction of Uncertainty.* Design is a processing of information that results in a transition from uncertainty about the success or failure of a design toward certainty.

(11) *Economic Worth of Evidence.* Information and its processing has a cost which must be balanced by the worth of the evidence bearing on the success or failure of the design.

(12) *Bases for Decision.* A design project (or subproject) is terminated whenever confidence in its failure is sufficient to warrant its abandonment, or is continued when confidence in an available design solution is high enough to warrant the commitment of resources necessary for the next phase.

(13) *Minimum Commitment.* In the solution of a design problem at any stage of the process, commitments which will fix future design decisions must not be made beyond what is necessary to execute the immediate solution. This will allow the maximum freedom in finding solutions to subproblems at the lower levels of design.

(14) *Communication.* A design is a description of an object and a prescription for its production; therefore, it will have existence to the extent that it is expressed in the available modes of communication.

Among the foregoing, there are principles of two kinds. Some are propositions that have a factual content.* They are factual because we can compare them with physical reality; thus their truth can be tested empirically. They describe what we believe is a proper generalization of some relevant part of physical reality. In the list, they are distinguished by the verb *is*. In terms of grammar they are in the indicative mood.

The remaining propositions have an ethical content. They reflect what we believe is a proper generalization of the values and mores of our culture. They are characterized by the auxiliary verb *must*. They are in the imperative mood, like the Ten Commandments; and like the Ten Commandments they can only be tested in a pragmatic sense. If people generally like the results, then we assume that the corresponding principles fit the ethics of our society. We might individually disagree with the particular ethics; if so, we have the right to seek, or to offer, the leadership that could persuade people to change them.

---

* The notions of factual and ethical contents of statements are set forth lucidly in Chapter III, "Fact and Value in Decision Making" of Herbert A. Simon's *Administrative Behavior* (New York: The Macmillan Company, 1958).

ENGINEERING DESIGN

AND THE ENVIRONMENT

INTERACTION OF DESIGN AND ENVIRONMENT

We have seen that engineering design responds to economic forces and technological advances. It is also responsive to the political, social, and other cultural factors that constitute the whole environment of society. It will be well to examine this environment which greatly affects the design project; at the same time we take note that the environment is itself reciprocally affected, in large measure or small, by the consequences of the design project. Some of the interactions between engineering systems and the environment, of which they become a part, are brought into focus in this chapter in order to illuminate those demands of society which bear on the designer.

THE SOCIO-ECOLOGICAL SYSTEM

A natural system of plant and animal life develops in a particular locale by constantly interacting with its environment. Indeed, the immediate environment must be counted as an integral part of the system if the latter is to be understood; for, as the biological community matures, it does more than react to the original environment; it begins to influence the environment. Heavy forest cover, encouraged to grow in soil made fertile by the humus of grasses and plants, filters out the sun and changes the micro-climate so that the original ground cover finds the new environment inhospitable, and as a result is partly supplanted by ferns and other shade-loving plants. Small animals feed on nuts and berries and on still smaller animal life. Larger predatory animals move into the community and thrive on the smaller animals. Eventually a climax condition is reached, and for a time, long or short, the dynamic interplay of many forces keeps the system in near balance. If disturbances of the various factors are relatively small, the system will maintain its state of quasi-equilibrium, adapting itself to slow secular changes in the physical and biological environment. If a major perturbation occurs, the system may become unstable and destroy itself. For example, the small animals may multiply because of a rich supply of food in a particularly productive year. Correspondingly, the predators multiply in proportion to the abundance of small animals. If the next year produces a very poor crop, the small animals may become virtually extinct

7

from both the lack of food and the ravages of the hungry, expanded population of predators. Furthermore, if small animals kept the pests of trees and other flora under control, their disappearance would permit exceptional destruction of the plant life and the entire system could be disrupted and indeed destroyed. The study of systems of biological entities interacting with their environment is known as ecology; and such systems are ecological systems. In socio-ecological systems the interest centers on social groups of people interacting with their environment. Of particular interest in this text is the manner in which the products of engineering design contribute to, and relate with, the socio-ecological systems.

THE SOCIO-ECOLOGICAL INFLUENCE ON ENGINEERING DESIGN

Industry produces, and commerce distributes, the goods and services that people consume. After consumption is completed, the waste products are removed. Usually they are destroyed; sometimes they are salvaged. In a non-human ecological system there are no waste products, for the cycle is closed and each component provides sustenance for another. Man is like a guest in the house of a generous and affluent host. There is abundance when the guests are few; but when they come flocking, a frugal charity replaces the open-handed giving. Depleted resources on the one hand, and on the other the pressures of growing populations in every part of the world, in addition to a rising determination of the have-nots to have, places a strain on a hitherto provident host that will make waste insufferable. Recovery, rather than disposal, of the end-products of consumption will increase in importance, thus closing the cycle more tightly.

Four processes: production, distribution, consumption, and recovery or disposal, form a production-consumption cycle, one of the main patterns in the socio-ecological system (Figure 2.1). It is by no means the only cycle; for there are many such. Each one reflects some aspect or activity in the life and environment of human society. The totality of the interlinked and interacting cycles comprises the socio-ecological system.

The production-consumption cycle is of particular interest to the engineering designer; for the products he designs must enter this cycle and must practically, without exception, be compatible with the four processes. Each process places its own set of demands on the design. Often the demands are contradictory, so that completely satisfying one of these unbalances the design with respect to some of the others. Reconciling conflicts which arise from this and from other sources is one of the principal problems of design. We shall meet such contradictory circumstances time and again, and the means by which they can be resolved will bear much discussion. Basically, the engineer designs for the consumer, who, if he were to withhold his acceptance, would spell certain failure for the product. To a large extent, therefore, the engineer addresses himself to the consumer; but at the same time he must view the design from the producer's

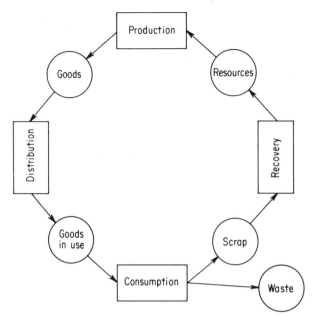

FIG. 2.1 Production Consumption Cycle.

side, who is usually also his employer. Whereas consumers' interests are concerned with ease of maintenance, reliability in use, longevity, appearance, and so on, the producer is concerned with ease of production, availability of resources, standardization of parts, and with reduction of rejections. The distributor has a view towards his desires; ease of transport, suitability for storage, long length of shelf-life, and attractiveness in display. Finally, the salvage-operator is concerned with ease of setting apart reusable materials and parts, and with economic disposal of the residue. The designer is obliged to take account in proper measure of these differing viewpoints, and to synthesize their separate objectives into a coherent design.

FLUX IN THE PRODUCTION-CONSUMPTION CYCLE

So far we have fixed our attention on the flux of physical objects in the production-consumption cycle. But two other sets of more abstract objects flow through the cycle also. One is a set of values. Consider a particular product. We begin the cycle with some resources. These may be raw materials, energy, amortizable production facilities, and human effort. Some amount of these economic factors is required to produce one unit of product. Associated with this amount is a value, generally measurable in dollars and usually called the cost of production. The emerging product also has a value measured in dollars and determined by the forces in the market place. The difference between output and input values, called

9

gross profit, provides an economic driving force which motivates the enterprise.

In a like manner there is a flux of value through the process of distribution, accompanied by an augmentation in value as measured in dollars, arising from a more favorable time and location for marketing. The consumer pays the final price, but he does so because the product has a greater worth to him than the purchase price. At this point we lose our objective measure of value. We can only hypothesize a subjective measure of value which economists have called utility. The lack of an objective measure poses grave conceptual difficulties, and is a recurring problem in engineering design: firstly, because of the designers' concern with setting values on the consumption process; and second, because all design decisions are based on logically organizable information admixed with intuition and judgment. When we deal with the element of judgement, as with the estimates of utility, we deal with subjective measures of value. Nonetheless, we will need to seek out the best tools with which to cope with such measures.

The second set of objects pertains to information; that this plays a major role in engineering design is clear when one considers that design is essentially a process of gathering and organizing information. The latent information, available for the effort and cost of gathering it at each point in the cycle, is of great importance for the redesign of products, or for the design of new products having some similar characteristics. Of equal importance is information about components, materials, processes, environments, and specifications. The task of maintaining the store of information in useful fashion is of huge proportions. The volume of new technical data generated each year is tremendous. The gathering, organizing, updating, storing, and retrieving of such data is so large an undertaking, and so critically important, that it has been proposed that a few immense design-data-processing centers be established at strategic locations. These proposed centers would be accessible to design offices throughout the nation via telephone connection, the information becoming available upon presentation of the properly-coded queries to the computers.

RANGE OF GOODS AND SERVICES

The discussion thus far has not been directed toward any particular field of design in engineering activity. This is intentional, for the content of this discourse is regarded as having enough generality to apply with proper force to all undertakings of engineering design whether they be concerned with such consumer products as automobiles and home appliances, or with heavy electrical and mechanical machinery; or with electronic components, devices, and systems like those used in communication work, computers, and controls; or with public works such as dams, highway systems, and sanitation systems; or with structures like buildings and homes, air and space craft; or with large and complex systems which combine many kinds of equipment into an integrated whole. Nor is the discussion limited to physical and tangible goods. It is regarded as applying to the design of service production whether it be the individual consumer's use of a telephone or a power system, or of an automatic car wash system, or of a supermarket.

Clearly, such diverse design projects will require specialized knowledge which derives from various areas of engineering subjects. The development of specialized knowledge of this kind is not contemplated in this book except as it is required for illustrating some examples. The concentration, as emphasized earlier, will be on those elements which belong in a discipline of design. This is a general introduction to the principles and theory of design, and, as such, is intended to lay a foundation for subsequent design work in later courses that lean heavily on one or the other of the various engineering specialties.

chapter

3 THE MORPHOLOGY OF DESIGN

THE DESIGN PROJECT

Each design-project has an individual history which is peculiarly its own. Nonetheless, as a project is initiated and developed, a sequence of events unfolds in a chronological order forming a pattern which, by and large, is common to all projects. We wish to examine this pattern, and to bring into sight the methodology of design by which ideas about needs are projected creatively into ideas about things; and which in turn are translated into engineering prescriptions for transforming suitable resources into useful, physical objects.

First we consider the overall pattern. A project goes through a series of major phases. Generally, a new phase is not begun until the preceding one has been completed, although sometimes final details have to be attended to while the next phase is in progress. Often, particularly when the project is large, much of the personnel will change with each new phase in order to bring to bear special skills and knowledge, and only a skeleton group, a project team, will remain permanently with the project. We will enumerate and describe these phases, sketching in briefly the steps of which they are composed. The morphology of design refers to the study of the chronological structure of design projects. It is defined by the phases (Figure 3.1) and their constituent steps. The steps of the design phases, having been put into perspective, will be enlarged in the following chapters.

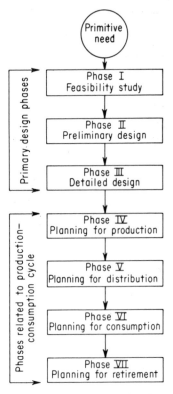

FIG. 3.1 **The Phases of a Complete Project.**

FEASIBILITY STUDY—PHASE I

A design project begins with a feasibility study; the purpose is to achieve a set of useful solutions to the design problem. Sometimes a design group is assigned to a project for which a design concept has already been fixed. This implies one of three possibilities: a feasibility study had been previously made; the technical management has had so much experience with the particular design problem that further study should be superfluous; the management, by omitting the feasibility study, is proceeding on unsupported intuition.

The first step in the study is to demonstrate whether the original need, which was presumed to be valid, does indeed have current existence, or strong evidence of latent existence. The next step is to explore the design problem engendered by the need and to identify its elements such as parameters, constraints, and major design criteria. In the following step an effort is made to conceive a number of plausible solutions to the problem. Finally, the potentially useful solutions are sorted out of the plausible set in three steps on the bases of physical realizability, economic worthwhileness, and financial feasibility. In conclusion, the completed study indicates whether a current or a potential need exists, what the design problem is, and whether useful solutions can be found; that is, it investigates the feasibility of the proposed project.

PRELIMINARY DESIGN—PHASE II

The preliminary design phase starts with the set of useful solutions which were developed in the feasibility study. The purpose of preliminary design is to establish which of the proffered alternatives is the best design concept. Each of the alternative solutions is subjected to order of magnitude analyses until the evidence suggests either that the particular solution is inferior to some one of the others, or that it is superior to all of the others. The surviving solution is tentatively accepted for closer examination. Synthesis studies are initiated for establishing, to a first approximation, the fineness of the range within which the major design parameters of the system must be controlled. Further studies investigate the tolerances in the characteristics of major components and critical materials which will be required to insure mutual compatibility and proper fit into the system. Other studies examine the extent to which perturbations of environmental or internal forces will affect the stability of the system.

Next, projective-type studies are undertaken, addressed to the question of how the solution will fare in time. The socio-economic conditions, such as consumers' tastes, competitors' offerings, or availability of critical raw materials, may change; the state of technical art may advance; and eventually corrosion, fatigue, and deterioration of performance may set in. Time will almost certainly erode the quality of the product. The question is, how fast? The rate of obsolescence or wear must be accounted one of the important design considerations, and its economic impact must be put in the balance. Finally, critical aspects of the design must be put to the test in order to validate the design concept and to provide essential information for its subsequent phases.

DETAILED DESIGN—PHASE III

The detailed design phase begins with the concept evolved in the preliminary design. Its purpose is to furnish the engineering description of a tested and producible design. Up to this point the design project was characterized by great fluidity. Major changes in concept could be accommodated without great financial loss. Indeed, for the first two phases such fluidity is essential, for they are primarily exploratory in nature, seeking to reveal an adequate range of possible solutions. At this point, however, either exploration on a large scale must come to a close, and a final decision for a particular design concept be made, or the project must be abandoned as infeasible. In the latter event, final abandonment if warranted by favorable circumstances, may be deferred pending the results of an additional search for possible new solutions.

With the design concept in mind and the preliminary synthesis information at hand, an overall, but provisional, synthesis is accomplished. It is developed as a master layout. With this as a basis the detailed design or specification of components is carried forward. From time to time, exigencies in the detailed work at the component level may dictate changes in the master layout; therefore it has provisional status. As the paper design progresses, experimental design is appropriately initiated. Experimental models are constructed to check out untried ideas which are not suitable to final disposition by analysis. Components, partial prototypes, and

13

finally complete prototypes are tested as the need for information arises. This information, accruing from the testing programs, provides a basis for redesign and refinement until an engineering description of a proven design is accomplished.

PLANNING THE PRODUCTION PROCESS—PHASE IV

Whereas the preceding three phases were peculiarly in the province of the engineering designer, much of the responsibility for phase IV will be shared with other segments of management. A new battery of skills, those of tool design and production engineering, come into play; the original project group, however, may continue in its role of leadership. The decision to produce often involves an enormous economic commitment. The level of confidence in the success of the product must be very high to support a positive decision. The decision itself must be made at that level of management at which the final responsibility for the success of the enterprse rests. The evidence on which the engineer, responsible for the design project, bases his confidence must be communicated in a condensed, but nevertheless fully revealing, form to the appropriate decision-maker. Ideally, the designer's confidence will be shared by the superior, who will re-evaluate this confidence using additional information concerning financial capability, business conditions, and like considerations, before rendering a final decision.

The production planning phase involves many steps which will vary in form and detail with the industry concerned. The following abbreviated list is typical of the mass production industries.

(1) Detailed planning of the manufacturing processes as required for every part, every subassembly, and the final assembly:–The information is usually displayed on process-sheets, one (or several if space requires it) for each part or sub-assembly. The process sheet contains a sequential list of operations which must be performed to produce the part; it specifies the raw material, clarifies special instructions, and indicates tooling and machines required. This step is particularly important, because design features that lead to difficulties in production are revealed. Such difficulties should have been minimized by previous timely consultations between product designers and tool designers. Similarly, questions about materials should have been resolved by consultation with process-metallurgists.

(2) Design of tools and fixtures:–This design work proceeds generally from the information developed in the operations analysis on the process sheets.

(3) Planning, specifying or designing new production and plant facilities.

(4) Planning the quality control system.

(5) Planning for production personnel:–Job-specifications are developed, standard times are determined, and labor costs are estimated.

(6) Planning for production control:–Work schedules and inventory

controls are evolved. Standard costs for labor, materials, and services, are established and integrated with the accounting system.

(7) Planning the information-flow system:–Information necessary for transmission of instructions and provision of feedback for control is determined. Appropriate forms and records are designed and integrated with computers when available. Flow patterns and routings are established.

(8) Financial planning:–Usually, large sums of money are required to initiate production of a new product. The source of the financing must be carefully established, and the means and rate of recovering the capital determined.

PLANNING FOR DISTRIBUTION–PHASE V

It will be recalled that production is the first process in the production-consumption cycle of the socio-ecological system. The second is distribution. Although the engineering designer may not be directly involved in planning for distribution, he will often find that the problems of distribution have an important impact on the original design of the product. It is often primary, as in the design of a water or electrical power system.

The purpose of this phase is to plan an effective and flexible system of distribution of the designed good. The abbreviated list is indicative of the planning for distribution.

(1) Designing the packaging of the product:–The outer shape of the product may be influenced by the need to effect economy in shipping costs. Individual and special packaging may be needed to secure protection from shock and weather. Special strapping and palletizing may be·needed to facilitate handling.

(2) Planning the warehousing system:–The economically favorable locations for warehouses are determined; the warehousing facilities are designed.

(3) Planning the promotional activity:–Technical sales brochures based on design information and test data may need to be developed.

(4) Designing the product for conditions arising in distribution:–Such factors as shelf-life, attractive display, and final conditioning before delivery to the consumer may affect design of the product. There may be a need of enough flexibility in the design to allow of special modifications to suit customers' needs, or of further adding available optional features as required by the customer, or for modular additions to the system to enlarge its capacity.

Clearly, some of the factors enumerated here cannot await consideration before the effort for this phase will have been fully mounted, but must instead be anticipated in the earlier phases.

PLANNING FOR CONSUMPTION–PHASE VI

Consumption is the third process in the production-consumption cycle. Its influence on design is profound, for it pervades all phases. As a process it occurs naturally after distribution. As a phase, in the time-pattern of the design project, most of the process of consumption must be anticipated in the early stages of design in order to have a timely impact. Therefore, it is for the most part a diffused phase concerned with consumers' needs and utilities, and mingled with and attached to the prior phases. It is set up separately only to emphasize some of the special contributions which it makes in addition to its more general and pervading influences. This separate status as a phase does not imply that consideration even of the steps enumerated here as belonging to the consumption phase is to be deferred until this late stage; in fact, for most of the steps, the contrary is true.

The purpose of this phase is to incorporate in the design adequate service features and to provide a rational basis for product-improvement and redesign. The steps follow.

(1) Design for maintenance.

(2) Design for reliability.

(3) Design for safety.

(4) Design for convenience in use (taking account of human factors).

(5) Design for aesthetic features.

(6) Design for operational economy.

(7) Design for adequate duration of service.

(8) Obtain service data that can provide a basis for product improvement, for next-generation designs, and for the design of different, but related, products.

PLANNING FOR RETIREMENT OF THE PRODUCT—PHASE VII

The fourth process in the production-consumption cycle is the disposal of the retired product. For large and semipermanent installations, the mere removal may pose difficult engineering problems, as, for example, the demolition of a tall building closely confined by a building on either side. Sometimes the impact on a new design is more immediate as when an old structure or system must be replaced by a new one with minimum disruption of normal operations.

What determines when an economic commodity in use, such as a consumer's product, a commercial or industrial device, or a private or public system, has reached an age at which it should be retired? This is one of the principal questions raised by a study of engineering economy. If the good in use has worn to the point at which it can no longer render adequate service, then the need of replacement is clear. However, the same fast pace of technology which presses upon the designer also accelerates the ageing process of goods in use. It is a peculiar mark of our times that goods in use are retired more frequently because of technical obsolescence than for physical deterioration. Changes in fashions, often deliberately cultivated by industry, also produce their share of casualties. In the design of soft goods, such as clothing, exploiting fashion changes is an accepted and respected practice, as the intrinsic value of such goods resides largely in their aesthetic appeal, but grave ethical questions are raised when obsolescence of style, unaccompanied by significant technical improvements, is used as a means of inducing the retirement of the products of engineering design.

To the engineering designer, the question whether to design for physical deterioration or for technical obsolescence is of fundamental importance. Ideally, the system should be designed so that it wears out physically as it becomes technically obsolescent; then no extra cost would be incurred by having provided for a longer than useful life. But usually, the elements of design that contribute to a longer life are also essential to adequate reliability and maintenance; thus a full balance between obsolescence and wear out is generally not possible. These aspects of design need further exploration.

What values are available when an economic good reaches a terminal point of service? And how do these values influence design? The latter question is the concern of the retirement phase in design. The purpose of this phase is to take account of the problems associated with retiring and disposing of a product. The same comments, made about the steps in the consumption phase reflecting their diffusion into the preceding phases, applies to most of the following steps.

(1) Designing to reduce the rate of obsolescence by taking into account the anticipated effects of technical developments.

(2) Designing physical life to match anticipated service life.

(3) Designing for several levels of use so that, when service life at a higher level of use is terminated, the product will be adaptable to further use at a less demanding level.

(4) Designing the product so that reusable materials and long-lived components can be recovered.

(5) Examining and testing of service-terminated products in the laboratory to obtain useful design information.

In summary, although the first three design phases, forming a primary set, are the principal concern of the design group, the remaining four, which constitute a secondary part stemming from the production-consumption cycle, have so great an impact on the design that they must be considered in detail in the total design effort. However, the steps of the secondary set of phases will not be developed further, but the steps of the primary set will be elaborated in greater deail in the ensuing text.

THE FEASIBILITY STUDY

We return to the primary design phases to look more closely at their constituent steps. The feasibility study with its steps and their inter-connections is presented in the flow diagram of Figure 4.1.

TNE NEED—ESTABLISHING ITS ECONOMIC EXISTENCE

The starting point of a design project is a hypothetical need which may have been observed currently on the socio-economic scene. It may be phrased in the form of a primitive statement resting on untested observations; or it may have been elaborated into a sophisticated and authenticated statement based on market and consumer studies. The need may not yet exist, but there may be evidence that it is latent, and that it can be evoked when economic means for its satisfaction become available. The need may be suggested by a technical accomplishment that makes the means of its satisfaction possible. In whatever way the need has been perceived, its economic existence, latent or current, must be established with sufficient confidence to justify the commitment of the funds necessary to explore the feasibility of developing the means satisfying it. By economic existence of a need we shall mean that individuals, institutions or society will recognize the need and will pay the price of the means which can satisfy it. The means may be available in the market place for a purchase-price, or it may be proffered by a government agency and paid for by taxation. The importance of establishing the need can hardly be overstated. Too often an organization will plunge into a project and develop a technical success while achieving a financial failure because the assumed need was ephemeral and disappeared in the light of reality.

Intuitive knowledge about people, their habits and mores, and their behavior in the socio-economic system, may be combined with specific information obtained by market research to provide the information for making a need analysis. After performing the need analysis (discussed in Chapter 8) a decision must be made about the validity of the economic existence of the need. The decision will be favorable if the weight of evidence is sufficient to induce a high enough level of confidence in the decision-maker (who may be the design engineer bearing the responsibility for the project). If it is favorable, the results of this step are summarized in a set

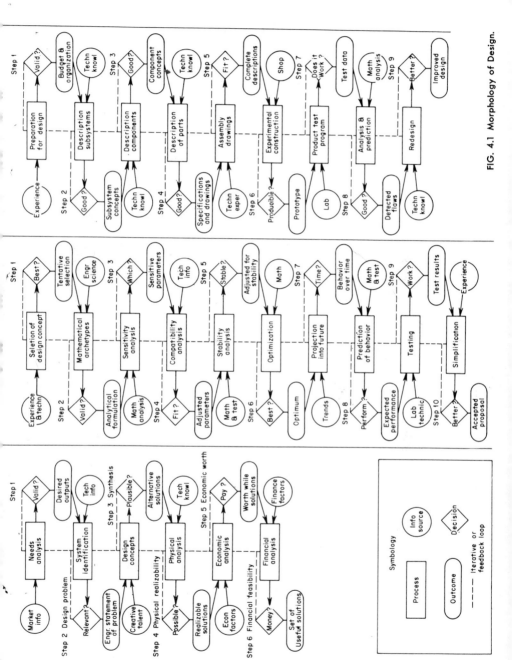

FIG. 4.1 Morphology of Design.

19

of specifications of desired outputs which the device or system must be capable of producing in order to satisfy the need.

THE DESIGN PROBLEM—IDENTIFICATION AND FORMULATION

Before an attempt is made to find possible solutions for the means of satisfying the need, the design problem should be identified and formulated. It is strange how strong the temptation is to seize mentally on some concept of hardware that seems to provide a feasible solution before the real problem is well understood, and thereafter to patch up the concept in perilous ways as deficiencies in the solution begin to appear. The temptation should be resisted, for it tends to lead to a mental rut which blocks the truly creative effort that should follow after the problem is grasped. In effect, we consider the ultimate solution to be a black box, the contents of which remain unknown. The information we have available comes from the results of the preceding step, particularly the specifications of desired outputs, and from relevant technical knowledge about environments, resources and general engineering principle. With this information an activity analysis (see Chapter 8) is performed whereby the design problem is given a technical formulation. The question which must be asked before this step may be considered complete is whether the resulting engineering statement of the problem is sufficiently relevant and adequate to commit the ensuing steps to the design. If the decision-maker is not confident enough, he will reject the statement and require another performance of the activity analysis step. Indeed, new information, developed in this step, may reduce the confidence in the validity of the preceding need analysis step and require further study at that level. This iterative nature, involving repetition of steps or parts of steps, is characteristic of design. Design is too complex a process to admit of an uninterrupted progression without backing up now and then to correct or rework previous results. New information is constantly developed by the design work itself which previously was either overlooked or unknown. This new information changes the confidence levels on which prior decisions were made. If the deterioration in confidence is enough to destroy the basis for a particular decision, the decision-maker will require that the affected step be reworked until the necessary level of confidence is restored.

THE SYNTHESIS OF POSSIBLE SOLUTIONS

Synthesis refers to the fitting together of parts or separate concepts to produce an integrated whole. The synthesis step formally begins after the design problem is well understood, although some notions about possible solutions may have already been suggested during the prior steps. The point to be emphasized is deceptively obvious; concentration on possible solutions should not begin until the design-problem has been studied and identified, and a reasonably good working formulation of the problem set down. As with prior steps, there is an iteration process, a feed-back. The solutions, which are conceived and matched against the background of the problem statement, yield new insights and items of information about the preceding steps which can then be corrected if necessary.

It is the synthesis step which most characterizes the project as a design undertaking. This, more than any other step, requires inventive and creative effort. Creativity is therefore a very essential ingredient of engineering design. In the context of design we offer the following as a definition of creativity: a talent for discovering combinations of principles, materials or components, which are especially suitable as solutions to the problem in hand. None of the individual elements which comprise the synthesis need be new or novel. Developing new and novel elements is more the object of research than of design. After a new principle is discovered by the researcher, the designer is often assigned the task of evolving some new components that are advantaged, for the first time made possible by the new principle. In doing so he will generally combine the new principle with several old ones to achieve the final result.

PHYSICAL REALIZABILITY

The outcome of the synthesis step is a set of plausible solutions. Each one of the set is a mental abstraction which takes account of some of the major factors or elements on which it depends. Omitted from such an idealization are many ancillary and consequent factors which may tip the balance towards success or failure. The problem is whether it is possible to accomplish such a practical physical embodiment as is suggested by the concept. The designer can visualize to a limited depth only the elements and results of a new concept, like the chess player who can see no more than a few moves ahead, only dimly perceiving all of the implications.

We assume that the solutions are plausible. By this we mean that the major elements of the concept could combine as visualized, in concordance with natural principles, to effect the solution; that is, in the overall view the concept could work in principle if the supporting elements could be realized. Thus the problem of establishing, on a sufficient level of confidence, the possibility of physical realization of a solution is transferred to a similar consideration of the constituent elements. This process of transferring attention to a lower order of sub-problems is a distinctive feature of the decision-process in engineering design and warrants fuller exposition (see Chapter 9, "Decision Processes in Design").

ECONOMIC WORTHWHILENESS

No object is a proper subject of engineering design if it is unable to pass the test of economic worth-whileness. Literally, this means that the object of the design must be ". . . of sufficient value to repay the effort."

(See *Webster's New International Dictionary, Unabridged,* Second Edition.) Value has a connotation which is singularly personal; it depends on the evaluator, his viewpoint, and the prevailing circumstances. The only objective measure is in the market place. When this instrument of measure can be applied, the results can be quantitatively reckoned and expressed in terms of dollars. Otherwise values remain subjective. Indirect tools, highly sophisticated and difficult to apply, must be used for their measure.

It is of interest to contrast the values of producer and consumer. The producer must acquire the requisite resources of raw materials, energy, capital, and manpower. These he can obtain on the open market; therefore their value of acquisition can be determined objectively. The final product, after its completion by transforming the input resources, is returned to the market place. Again, the value can be determined, and the input-output values compared. If the flux of values through the production process has occasioned an augmentation of value sufficient to induce its continuance, the process is deemed to be economically worth-while. The extension to the distributor follows in the same manner.

The consumer can likewise measure the value of acquisition by the cost of the product in the market place. With this product he can satisfy appropriate needs. But how does he, or a detached observer, measure the value of this gratification? Clearly the value is subjective and cannot be measured in the market place; therefore the objective monetary value of the cost is not commensurable with the subjective use value. We can only infer economic worthwhileness by the continued willingness of buyers to pay the purchase price. Nevertheless, the designer must predict as best he can the intensity of the economic worth-wileness to consumers in general so that he can estimate the market potential; for his choice of a design concept must be conditioned by the economic worth-whileness of each and all of the chief protagonists in the production-consumption cycle. It is for this reason that the designer must be prepared and able to place himself mentally in the economic and psychological states of each in turn: producer, distributor, and consumer. As he visualizes himself in each role, he must extract the essential contributions to the design which each view-point offers. Clearly, those solutions which do not pass the test of economic worth-whileness at the three major nodes of the production-consumption cycle are eliminated from the list of acceptable solutions.

Further exploration in depth within an engineering framework of economic worth-whileness, with its dependence on time, service life, and obsolescence, is the proper subject matter of Engineering Economy. The subject will be pursued here only to the extent that an exposition of the design undertaking demands.

FINANCIAL FEASIBILITY

Sometimes it happens that a project, meritorious from every point of view, and of great economic worth, cannot be realized because the financial resources for its prosecution cannot be mustered. Public works, depending on bond issues, abandoned when finances are not forthcoming, is a case in point. Similar instances often occur in private enterprise. Before substantial commitments are made for design work the project should be examined for financial feasibility. It may well be that some of the proffered solutions will lead to greater financial demands than others; some may require greater financial resources than are available, and thus be abandoned.

The last three steps are like sieves. Through the first sieve are passed only those solutions which are physically realizable; through the second, only those possessing economic worth-whileness for producer, distributor and consumer; through the third, only those that are financially feasible. The set of useful solutions comprises the ones passing successfully through each of the three sieves.

In fine, the feasibility study is the first major phase of a design project. It establishes whether the problem posed by the project is soluble and whether there are solutions that are likely to be useful. It is accomplished in a series of design steps any one of which may be repeated, subject to economic considerations, until the interactions of successive steps have been properly accommodated. The first two steps, which emphasize the gathering and organizing of information, are: validating and expanding a primitive statement of need into an engineering specification of outcomes, and formulating the central problem of the project and identifying critical overall design variables, constraints, relationships, and criteria. The next step emphasizes synthesis and is directed toward evolving a set of possible solutions that are plausible in the light of an understanding of the problem. The next three steps emphasize evaluation and eliminate, in turn, those solutions which are unlikely to be:—firstly, physically realizable; second, economically worthwhile; and third, financially feasible. The result is a set of useful solutions.

THE PRELIMINARY DESIGN

The preliminary design is intended to establish an overall concept for the project which will serve as a guide for the detailed design. An evaluation of the design concept is carried forward far enough so that a decision can be made about committing funds for the next phase. The preliminary design phase is shown diagrammatically in Figure 4.1.

SELECTION OF THE DESIGN CONCEPT—STEP 1

In the set of useful solutions, developed in the feasibility study, the most promising one must be identified. If further study strengthens the evidence that its promise will be fulfilled, it is provisionally adopted as the design concept for the project. The first step, therefore, is to compare the several useful solutions in order to select one as the best tentative concept. In principle, the approach is straightforward; in practice, the decision is difficult. In principle, the advantageous and disadvantageous attributes of each solution are listed and the one with the most favorable set is selected; in practice, the following difficulties arise:

(1) How can we know whether the attributes we list are relevant to the comparisons of the rival solutions? How can we know that we have included all that are important?

(2) From whose point of view shall we judge the advantage of a particular attribute?

(3) What values should we associate with each relevant attribute? How can these values be combined?

(4) With how much confidence can we assert that a particular design concept can be carried through to a physically realizable design?

(5) To what other design problems does the solution under scrutiny give rise? Will these new subproblems be resolvable into solutions which can be physically realized?

The first question deals with design criteria which can be used as instruments for testing relevancy and importance. The third deals with setting up measures of value. The fourth and fifth questions raise issues about probabilities and outcomes which will be the concern of Chapter 9, "Decision Processes in Design." The second question has been discussed in Chapter 2, "Engineering Design and the Environment." The resolution of these questions involves philosophical and operational hazards. But progress in dealing with such matters quantitatively has come in recent years, although judgment still plays a major role in decision making and value setting. The way in which the synthesis of answers to these questions is accomplished will be deferred to the chapter on the decision process.

FORMULATION OF MATHEMATICAL MODELS OR ARCHETYPES—STEP 2

Design proceeds from the abstract to the concrete. It begins with a concept, conjured up in the mind; a relationship among ideas or geometrical forms which somehow fit the circumstances of the problem. Such mental abstractions can eventually become manifest in physical objects, but the bridge is a long one, and the first step over it is to bring the original idea into some form of communicable expression. We do this by describing the idea in words, in graphic illustrations, and in mathematical symbols. The very act of giving expression to a mental image endows that image with some of the essence of reality, creates of it an object which can be manipulated and combined with like objects. The concept becomes information which can exist in its own right. The information may still be abstract, but it is one step closer to the concrete.

As useful as verbal descriptions and graphic illustration are, symbolic descriptions are uniquely useful, for they can be manipulated with the facility of mathematical logic in pursuing the implications which are dormant in the concept. Although the implications may be perceived, they are often so involved and complex as to defy the power of the unaided mind to penetrate their nature. The symbolic description becomes a device which enables the designer to use information about the concept in order to anticipate analytically the behavior of the prototype. In this sense, the symbolic description becomes a mathematical archetype of the physical object which is yet to be materialized.

A single symbolic or analytical description of the design concept may be, and usually is, inadequate to portray the several facets of behavior. Therefore several descriptions are required, each one taking account of one physical or economic aspect; thus, simplicity is preserved as far as is possible. The set of descriptions are manipulated in an abstract manner as if they were the actual object, the outcomes thus obtained being ascribed to the real situation.

Only the simplest of systems or devices can be carried through in the transition from mind to physical reality without the help of mathematical descriptions. Such abstract archetypes merit more discussion (see Chapter 10, "Archetypes and Computers"); their formulation requires skill and ingenuity; their use is essential in the design steps that follow.

We visualize a system as being described in terms of a set of system variables or, as we shall call them, *design parameters*. The description will be in the form of equations, a mathematical archetype, involving the design parameters and the input and output variables. We would like to know how sensitive the performance of the system is to the adjustment of the several design parameters; those which critically affect the performance must be carefully adjusted, whereas other, less critical ones can be set to suit convenience.

The design parameters represent various attributes of the system; some may stand for critical dimensions, others for important properties or capacities, and some for possible states of the system. A specific design is accomplished in an abstract sense by giving to the design parameters a specific combination of values which are permissible within the circumscriptions of the system constraints.

Now we would like to know how the system will behave. To reveal the behavior, we choose some values for inputs to the system, that is, for the independent variables, and solve the equations for outputs, which are the dependent variables. In effect, this implies that a given set of values, applied to the input variables, will result in a concomitant set of values for the output variables; furthermore, changes imposed on the input variables will induce some corresponding changes in the output variables. But the pattern of correspondence between input and output variables is precisely what is meant by performance; and this, it is important to note, depends on the particular values assigned to the design parameters–that is, performance depends on the specific design.

The ability to manipulate a symbolic archetype leads to economy, convenience, and speed in the earlier stages of a design. The accomplishment of the same results by varying the elements of a physical prototype would be costly and slow, and sometimes impossible. In the later stages of a design, the balance may change and economy and speed may favor the testing and manipulation of physical models.

The results of the sensitivity analysis step are: greater insight to the inner workings of the system or device; an identification of the critical design parameters as distinct from the less critical; an indication whether some of the constraints should be loosened or tightened; a more quantitative idea about the expected overall performance of the system. Completion of this step will produce more evidence which may either strengthen the confidence in the design concept or cast doubt on its efficacy. The provisional status of the solution may be removed; it may be retained as still tentative; or the solution may be rejected on the basis of new, unfavorable evidence.

A system or a complicated device can be thought of as an object which is, itself, a combination of objects on the next lower order of complexity. In the case of a complex system such objects would be referred to as subsystems. The subsystems may be combinations of components which, in turn, may be combinations of parts. A very complex system will usually have an hierarchial structure many layers deep. The design of the overall system requires an examination of at least the first-order elements which compose it. In general, this is true at any stage of the design; when components are being designed, the parts thereof must be examined. A combination of elements implies a set of coacting objects. In order for the coaction or interaction to occur successfully, the individual objects must be compatible with their comembers.

Compatibility may involve straightforward considerations such as geometrical tolerances (the journal dimensions to ensure a proper fit in a bearing) or tolerances on physical characteristics (the resistance of a fixed resistor in a bridge circuit) or chemical tolerance (two dissimilar metals in contact). More difficult problems of compatibility arise when interacting comembers must have matching operating characteristics, as when one member is in series with another so that the outputs of one are the inputs of the other.

The problems of compatibility cover a wide spectrum. Examination in detail of any one of the many kinds of problems is beyond the scope of this text; such discussions must be left to more specialized treatments of specific kinds of designs. However, one important observation can be made; the design parameters which exhibited the least critical effect in the sensitivity analysis can receive the major adjustments in accommodating the subsystems or components to enhance mutual compatibility.

STABILITY ANALYSIS—STEP 5

The systems and devices that engineers design are exposed and must respond to the vagaries of a dynamic environment. For example a building is apparently a stable and static structure, but an earthquake may apply an impulsive displacement to the foundation, or a fire may suddenly raise the temperature of a critical column; or a suspension bridge may sway dangerously when a high and gusty wind applies a periodic succession of loads at the right frequency. Again, the wing of an airplane may begin to flutter at a certain speed, causing severe fatigue damage; or a freeway may bear a transient surge of traffic from an entrance ramp, suddenly bringing traffic to a halt.

We would like the systems we design to have an inherent stability so that uncommon perturbations in the environment, or accidentally large inputs or loads, will not cause catastrophic failures or malfunctions. We would prefer to have the system respond to the unusual circumstance, in whatever way it must, and then return to its normal equilibrium configuration. How large a perturbation should the system be able to cope with? This question raises statistical problems and value judgments about risks and public safety. Should we design a building within minimal standards of safety to withstand the shock of an earthquake that is expected to occur once in ten years, one hundred years, or once in a thousand years? We are led again to the questions of values and decisions.

The physical problem of stability can arise in either of two ways. It may reside solely in one of the subsystems or components or it may come about from the characteristics of the interactions among several of the subsystems. The first case is exemplified by loading a steel column axially. The column will return to its stable configuration when the perturbing load subsides, unless the load exceeds a critical level, whereupon a catastrophic failure occurs by buckling of the web. The second mode is typified by an automatically controlled machine in which the servo-mechanism interacts with some machine elements to effect control. If the perturbing force is of sufficient magnitude and unfavorable frequency, the error signal from the machine elements and the correcting action of the control device may come into phase in such a way as to reinforce the error and cause a disastrous malfunctioning.

The purpose of the stability analysis is to explore the behavior of the system in such a way as: firstly, to make sure that the system as a whole is not inherently unstable; second, to determine the regions which are inherently unstable in the design parameter space to insure their avoidance; third, to evaluate the risks and consequences of environmental disturbances which might be sufficient to cause catastrophic failures or malfunctions; and, last, to provide further evidence, for or against, the final choice of the particular design concept.

FORMAL OPTIMIZATION—STEP 6

Hitherto we have not tried to fix all of the major design parameters at definite and singular values. However, for the design to advance the parameters must receive specific design values. For some of the parameters this will imply a rigid fixing at a single value, as in the case of the diameter of a heat exchanger shell; for others, some natural fluctuations may occur in the normal operation of the system, but a design value is selected for the mean, as exemplified by the design voltage for a power transmission line; for still others, means will be provided for adjusting parameters manually or automatically over a range centered on the design value. This occurs, for example, in setting the speeds of the successive stands of a continuous rolling mill. One way of fixing the design value is by simply choosing any feasible combination which is thought to be convenient. Sometimes, when analytical methods are not available or the design must be completed in a very short time, such intuitive selection is the only recourse. However, we may suppose that among all of the feasible combinations of parameter values (that is, combinations which satisfy all of the design constraints and therefore could be expected to work) there is one superior to all others–the optimum combination. The process for finding this desideratum is named *optimization*. It can be obtained through trial and error by modifying successive generations of designs; by experimental methods in which parameters are changed in a consistent fashion so that the feasible parameter space can be explored; by mathematical means whereby the optimum is isolated (see Chapter II, "Techniques of Optimization"); and by computer simulation which is an abstract counterpart of the experimental method (see Chapter 10, "Archetypes and Computers").

In principle, a final discrimination among the several alternatives to find the best solution is only possible by comparing the optimum manifestations of each, but in practice the earlier probes reveal some solutions to be inferior to others (they are said to be dominated), and these certainly should be dropped as soon as the evidence warrants. Some rough approximations of optima can be made in the first tentative decision step of the preliminary design in order to sharpen the discrimination. If, however, several contending solutions have yet eluded rejection, the formal optimization step provides additional evidence for selecting the prime solution.

As soon as we raise the problem of finding which of the feasible solutions is best, we are forced to state with precision the rules by which we are to judge the vague quality of excellence. We must name and define the attributes which are to be considered, we must specify how they are to be measured, and we must establish their relative importance. We will refer to such a composite statement as the design criterion. If the optimization is to be performed mathematically, these considerations must be set forth in an equation which we shall call the *criterion function*.

In conclusion, the formal optimization step provides additional evidence, usually conclusive, for fixing the final design concept; it enables a selection, among all feasible combinations of values for the design parameters, of the set which yields the best results as specified by the overall design criterion.

PROJECTIONS INTO THE FUTURE–STEP 7

Prophecy, long before the seven dreams of Joseph, was one of the chief preoccupations of mankind. It was beset with many hazards then; it still is. The work of design demands a constant peering ahead through the curtains of time; for a project started in the present will not be completed until some time in the future, and the actual product will not be used until an even more remote time. Two main questions should be asked: one concerns the socio-economic environment that will exist when the product comes into actual use; the other refers to the race against technical obsolescence.

Economic, cultural and political trends have a bearing on the first question. Factors such as population growth, increase in gross national product, changes in recreational and work patterns, rate of family formation, shifts in relative numbers of urban and suburban residents, changes in policy on foreign aid and national defense and many other matters shape the future. Engineers who are responsible for projects have the obligation to try, with the aid of social scientists, to estimate the impact of these factors of social change on the products which they design.

It is said of some products that they are obsolete at the time when the design drawings are completed. This has been especially true in the fast-paced defense industry where international competition punctuates the design effort with grim reminders of national security. But it is becoming equally true of engineering design in many other industries; computers, machine tools, air transport, communications, and automation, to name a few. The designer has the obligations of staying abreast of advances in the relevant technology. He must sense the direction and the rate of technical development. He cannot, in general, commit his design beyond the current, or immediately foreseeable, state of the art, but he must attempt to accommodate the design to the impact of relentless change in such a way as to secure the greatest practical protection against the inroads of obsolescence. The possibilities, which can be exploited, are:–the use of the most advanced design compatible with technical and economic risk; the favoring of designs that enable the system to be utilized for secondary functions when it becomes obsolete for its primary use; the inclusion of some provisions which will enable future internal modifications to accommodate technical advances; the provision of compatibility with new components or subsystems that can be added in the future; the intensification of development work in directions where imminent breakthroughs are anticipated.

PREDICTION OF SYSTEM BEHAVIOR—STEP 8

In the preceding section we attended to the future effects of the technical and socio-economic environments on the system. But we have also to examine how the system itself will behave in the future by virtue of its own inherent characteristics. We design a system with the goal of being able effectively by means of it to produce a certain set of desired outputs in a particular range of environments. Usually, it is only possible to make substantial predictions about the physical performance, operational characteristics, and production costs of the system after the design concept has been carried through the preliminary design phase. Many designers are satisfied if they can demonstrate that the system, when built or manufactured, will be able to meet a set of acceptance specifications. It is, of course, important to make such predictions reliably. However, a system must function in an acceptable manner throughout a reasonable service life. To rephrase this point, the desired outputs must be produced over a span of time as well as at the start when the system is new. The actual outputs that the system has the capacity to produce must be regarded as a function of time so that their deterioration can be taken into account in assessing the real performance of the system.

The service life of a system or a device is measured rationally by considering the duration in which the net utility of its ownership (the excess in value of use utility of a device over the negative utility of acquiring, operating and maintaining it) is greater than for any other equivalent or substitutable means. A full elaboration of this concept is properly within the province of Engineering Economics. Here it will suffice to point out that the actual life in a particular instance may be determined by wear-out (physical life) or by diseconomy (when the cost of operation and maintenance exceeds the value of the use) or by obsolescence (when more economic and technically better means become available). In a stagnant technology devices tend to be replaced when they are deemed to be physically worn out; in a fast moving technology devices are usually replaced because they become obsolete. Often, it is possible to effect economies for the consumer, and to enhance the competitive position of the producer, by achieving a careful balance in the design between physical life and obsolescence. It is clearly of no benefit to the consumer to pay the extra cost of a lasting device if he, in reality, will discard it in a short time because of obsolescence.

TESTING THE DESIGN CONCEPT—STEP 9

The proof of the pudding is in the eating; the proof of a design is in the use of the product. Evolutionary design waits for the evidence which use reveals. But the lapse between the original bold and primitive essay and the final sophisticated version may be many generations. New design cannot wait, for it relies much more on innovation; and innovation, riding on the current crest of technical advance, must speed ahead or be overtaken and obsolesced by the next wave of new technical art.

Information about the performance of the products of the designer's art which could be gathered leisurely in a consumer's world during the time of a slower era, must be gotten much more speedily so that it can influence the immediate design. The recourse is the testing laboratory. The environment which will bear upon the product is reproduced. Time and space may be contracted to fit the confines and convenience of the laboratory, or time and space may be enlarged when the subject of the test is microcosmic. Familiar examples are:–the great increase of the frequency of operational cycles so that the life pattern of the product can be explored in a shortened span of time; the creation of a more severe environment (in respect to corrosion, stress, and other factors) in order to exhibit unfavorable results sooner; the reduction of the physical size of an object, like a model of an aircraft wing, so that it can fit in a wind tunnel test chamber; the examination with slow motion pictures of the vibrational behavior of a machine element.

Testing is not limited to proving acceptable performance; it is also the arbiter of questions regarding physical realizability of the system or its

31

components when such cannot be resolved by analysis or past experience. Experimental design refers to a test or development program which accompanies and is guided by the design project. It is a powerful extension of paper and pencil design; it serves to verify design hypotheses, to generate new design information, to develop improvements of the design concept, and to expose difficulties which might have been overlooked in the paper design.

Testing and experimental designing are generally more costly in money and time than paper design; therefore they should be considered as augmenting, supplementing, and verifying the latter, when the technical needs and the economic factors fully justify their use. Elaborate experimental programs are sometimes undertaken to obtain answers which could be found from simple experiments. Often a full exploration of the design parameter space is impractical or too costly. Proper planning in a statistical sense can greatly reduce the cost and size of an experimental program and, at the same time, increase the validity of the results. We shall refer to such planning as the *design of experiments*, although in the current statistical literature this is often called experimental design. We wish to avoid confusion by reserving the term, *experimental design*, exclusively for the experimental program which accompanies a design project.

SIMPLIFICATION OF DESIGN

As a design moves through the various steps, the original concept inevitably becomes more complicated. The simple and the obvious are hard to achieve. The solutions which first present themselves are involved and difficult and clamor for acceptance because better alternatives do not seem to be available. Of all questions, one of the most important for the designer to ask is whether the projected solution is the simplest to accomplish the desired result.

Quite often the inclusion of secondary requirements in the set of desired outputs gives rise to unnecessary complexity. They may have been added originally because it was felt that these ancillary benefits would be obtained with very little difficulty. However, after the design effort has progressed, the secondary nature of the added requirements is easily forgotten and the resulting complications accepted as unavoidable. Sometimes the assumption of unrealistic constraints or of unnecessarily severe environments or of subproblems which do not actually exist may lead to devious and intricate solutions.

Before the preliminary design can be considered to have been completed, it should be subjected to a rigorous study to reveal any unnecessary complicating factors and to discover every possible simplification. Good design has an aesthetic quality–the quality of simplicity.

The preliminary design begins with a decision problem–to select the best of the proffered solutions. In the second step we set up mathematical

32

archetypes of the chosen concept; and in the next three steps subject the archetypes to sensitivity, compatibility, and stability analyses. In the sixth step we optimize the archetypal representation. In the seventh step we attempt to gauge how the system will measure up to the standards of excellence in the future; and in the eighth we try to predict how the system will perform under the various kinds of conditions in which it may operate. In the ninth step we resort to experimental design and subject critical parts of the design concept to the hard realities of physical test, the results being used to revise the design concept if necessary. Finally, in the tenth step, we consider every possible way to simplify the design concept before submitting it as the proper solution for further development in the detailed design phase which follows.

chapter

6 | DETAILED DESIGN PHASE

The detailed design (see Figure 4.1) carries the overall design concept, developed in its preliminary stage, to the final hardware. To do so the overall concept must be brought to a state of design that is clearly physically realizable. This state is achieved by finally constructing a prototype from a full set of design instructions, testing it and making the necessary revisions in both prototype and design instructions until the system or device is satisfactory for production, distribution, and consumption.

PREPARATION FOR DESIGN—STEP 1

We start on the assumption that the overall concept of the system has been firmly fixed, that the subsystems have been tentatively defined, and that a provisional commitment has been made to execute a complete design; but in order to go ahead we need budgets and a design organization.

The commitment to proceed is provisional because relatively close estimates are required of the cost in time and money to carry out the design, the budgets for the design work depending on these estimates. For practical reasons it is only the management, who, having the responsibility for the final economic success of the project, can make the decision to suspend the project, or to approve the necessary budgets. Such estimates were also needed when the feasibility study and the preliminary design were made; the commitments were small, however, and the work was exploratory, so rough estimates were adequate. But the detailed design requires the commitment of much larger resources in the way of technical people, money, and time. The estimates need to be sufficiently reliable so that they can be used by management at face value. An estimate, recognized as necessarily tentative, is also required for the manufacturing cost.

Too often, management finds that engineers are likely to be much too optimistic about costs at the start of a project; consequently they are inclined to compensate this error in judgement by using a large, indiscriminate contingency factor. The practice is to be deplored, because projects may be rejected as unprofitable, owing to overcompensation, while others, less meritorious, are accepted because the compensatory factor was not large enough. Moreover, it is the engineer in charge of the project who should bear the responsibility of an accurate estimate. The management, by making unfactual corrections, tacitly relieves him of this burden, thereby encouraging him further to underestimate. Although it is a routine matter to estimate the cost of an item after it has been fully designed and when its manufacture is accomplished with known processes and materials, it is much more difficult to make accurate estimates for a design project whose central concept is still abstract and whose final form is still conjectural. The art and science of estimation is very under-developed and needs much attention.

Besides a committed monetary budget and an accepted period of time until the date of completion, we need to mobilize the technical and supportive manpower to perform the design work. The subject of organization for a design project is of prime importance, but a full treatment is beyond the scope of this text. A large design undertaking involves many people. Complications in communication and in coordination of effort become immediately evident. Many design decisions must be made, but their consequences range widely in importance. The authority to make decisions must be apportioned among the several levels of technical supervision so that the level of the decision-maker and the importance of the decision are properly related. Finally, there is the problem of interrelating the generalist and the specialist, the project team and the engineering departments. The problem is usually resolved for the larger projects by assigning a project manager to head the design effort under the chief engineer. Under the project manager is a team of generalists who develop the overall design concepts, but who call upon the specialist capabilities of the engineering department and the experimental and testing laboratories as needed in the course of the project.

In order to facilitate the preparatory work and to lay the foundation for the next step, that of subsystem design, a provisional master layout is

34

required which, in effect, presents in drawings the results of the preliminary design. Its provisional status reminds us that it will change in detail as the subsystems, components and parts are actually designed.

OVERALL DESIGN OF SUBSYSTEMS—STEP 2

In the preliminary design we were concerned with the overall concept; subsystems were examined only for the purpose of evaluating the quality of the overall system concept. Now each subsystem must be looked at as an individual entity. In effect the design of each subsystem follows the same general pattern as the preliminary design of the system, although requirements for compatibility and proper coaction among the constituent subsystems impose much tighter constraints upon them than did the environmental factors on the system as a whole. Another tight constraint is the design budget, each subsystem being assigned its appropriate share. A strong effort will be expected from each group leader to comply with its limits.

Alternative design concepts consonant with the overall system concept must be conceived for each subsystem, and they are subjected to the same decision process used in the system concept selection. The solution tentatively selected is analyzed for its sensitivity, compatibility and stability. It is optimized in much the same way as was the system, and subjected to the same scrutiny for possibilities of simplification. To accomplish these operations, each of the selected subsystems must be formulated as mathematical archetypes, unless such a formulation would be immaterial to the design work. A caution about optimizing subsystems is necessary. Unless the constraints imposed by the system as a whole, and by the requirements for compatibility, are fully recognized in the optimization, a so-called suboptimization may result that will not necessarily inure advantageously to the system as a whole. The same comment applies to components and parts.

Finally, a provisional master layout is prepared for each subsystem which translates into drawings the results of the subsystem designs. These master layouts become the basis for developing the design of the components.

OVERALL DESIGN OF COMPONENTS—STEP 3

The work which is required for the overall design of components is practically a repetition of what has been indicated for the subsystems. Just as the system comprises several subsystems, so the subsystems usually comprise some number of components, which are developed in much the same way as the subsystem. But as we move down to successively lower levels in the design project, the objects we deal with become progressively less abstract, and our concern with ultimate hardware becomes more immediate. Some of the components can even be purchased as complete assemblies of hardware, although this will not relieve us from making the original decisions involved in their selection, or from the several analyses which determine their place in the subsystems containing them.

As in the case of the subsystem, the results of the component designs are encompassed in provisional master layouts which are the basis for the detailed design of parts.

DETAILED DESIGN OF PARTS—STEP 4

Parts are the elementary pieces from which components are assembled. It is here, in the work of designing parts, that we come to grips with the concrete realities of hardware. In the design of subsystems or components, a huge number of relatively minor questions about achieving physical realization are allowed to go unanswered because we feel very sure that answers will come from sources of immediately accessible knowledge and from available experience in the technology when the actual parts are being designed. Thus, we concentrate, as we must if we are not to be frustrated and completely immobilized by innumerable details, on the overall concepts. Only such questions whose solutions are not obvious in the well-known technology receive our attention. Even the solutions to those questions are explored only until the obscure points have been cleared and we become confident that the design concept can be physically realized. But when a part is being designed, no questions pertaining to its design may remain unanswered; no ambiguities about its shape, its material, or its treatment may cloud the instructions for its manufacture. We have come to the place, on the long path from the abstract to the concrete, from the concept of the system or device to the physical embodiment thereof, where the final transition is made, where the idea merges into physical reality.

Although in the design of an individual part we are close to the physical terminus on the way from the abstract, critical parts may still require extensive analysis. The general physical embodiment of the part may appear clearly to the mind, but ways of giving it a useful symbolic description must yet be sought. Because of the tight constraints, a projected part has much greater definition when the initial consideration is made than either subsystems or components. For this reason, translating its design concept into symbolic terms is close to effecting a mathematical description of an existing object, an operation usually not too hard to accomplish. The same kinds of questions about sensitivity, and stability which arose at the higher levels of design are often important here, and for critical parts, optimization is almost always important. The problems of compatibility and simplification have special status in the design of parts. They lead to questions about tolerances in dimensions, mechanical, physical and chemical properties, composition of materials, and quality of workmanship. The association with production cost is close, for tighter tolerances beget higher prices.

Other problems of engineering design also become prominent. The part designer has close ties to the metallurgist, the production process engineer, and the tool designer. The choice of material for the part must be settled upon; its heat treatment and its surface treatment must be prescribed, if such are to be applied. The producibility of the part must be considered; and, at least in a general way, the production processes established for its manufacture. The general means of production need to be thought through, for they reflect on the manufacturing capabilities of the company and on the tooling costs that will be incurred in the preparation for production.

The detailed drawings afford an opportunity for careful checking. The designer, immersed in the manifold details of his design, and, if he has been properly motivated, emotionally involved in its outcome, is often unable to see some of the minor faults. The checker is a designer by training who has become a specialist in ferreting out minor flaws and, occasionally, large ones in the detailed and assembly drawings. He is the professional critic of the design project and his role is analogous to that of the critic in the world of letters and arts.

Complete definition of the parts is mandatory. The shop, it must be remembered, manufactures parts; the components, the subsystems and finally the system are, so far as the shop is concerned, only assemblies of parts. A part is defined by its description, which must be complete enough to prescribe precisely what it should be like after its manufacture. To accomplish this purpose we may need any or all of the following forms of description: detailed drawings, specifications, special instructions, standard symbols, notes, special sketches, and revisions or modifications.

PREPARATION OF ASSEMBLY DRAWINGS—STEP 5

It is only after the constituent parts have been designed that the form of a component can be fixed. The provisional layout of the component can now be replaced by a tentatively final assembly drawing. In producing the assembly drawing, cases of incompatibility, oversights in the compatibility analyses, will generally be revealed. The affected parts are suitably revised.

After the component assemblies are prepared, the corresponding assembly drawings for the subsystems can be drafted. Again, incompatibilities and misfits of various kinds may be revealed, and these are corrected by the same iterative process. Finally, the grand assembly for the system is similarly undertaken.

An aspect of physical realizability that is easily overlooked, at least in part, is in the spatial relations among the parts in the act of assembly. We sometimes find ourselves in the same situation as the man who built a boat in his workshop only to find that there was no way to remove the boat, short of tearing out a wall. The assembly drawings provide a visual aid to the difficult task of mentally visualizing the assembly operations and attempting to perceive whether assembly difficulties will arise.

At this time the expected manufacturing cost can be estimated more accurately. Management will usually wish this to be done for several reasons. With the new, and presumably more reliable, estimate, management can provisionally set a selling price for the purpose of exploring the potential market more carefully. Furthermore, the next steps involve building one or more prototypes for experimental purposes and embarking on an extensive test program. Such work is costly, and this is a convenient time for management to reappraise the economic worthwhileness of the proposed product. If the results of the reappraisal seem to be negative, the management could rescind approval of the project and order its abandonment or postponment. If it sustains its approval, then financial planning will be undertaken at the appropriate level of management for implementing the program and for reassessing financial feasibility.

For some types of projects, constructing small-size models instead of producing assembly drawings has proven to be cheaper, faster, and more useful in translating the design into construction. Some engineering firms and the engineering departments of some large chemical firms responsible for designing petroleum refineries, chemical plants, nuclear power plants and the like have found this to be true. Piping drawings are particularly complicated in such projects. In the models, miniature tubing or wire, in proper scale, is formed and set up to make the multitude of connections, using appropriate, scaled-down, plastic pipe fittings. Suitable colors identify the various piping circuits. The connections are made on the model without the use of drawings, merely by fitting the miniature pipe and pipe fittings to the various scaled components and subsystems. After the model is fabricated as an exact representation of the projected plant, it is taken to the site and used as a source of information for replicating the actual plant.

EXPERIMENTAL CONSTRUCTION—STEP 6

With the completed drawings at hand the experimental shop can undertake to build the first full-scale prototypes. Sometimes the first prototype is also the end-product. A project involving the design of a large office building, of a production plant, of custom-built machinery, of a public works, of a ship, and of other similar undertakings often falls into this category. In such cases the design will be changed and revised to overcome difficulties, which usually are, and generally should be restricted to, problems of physical realizability, that are revealed as the construction and fabrications go forward. A supervising engineer, who attempts to anticipate the difficulties, and a field design staff, sized appropriately to the project, whose function is to effect the revisions, are attached to the project at the construction site. Nearly every revision has manifold consequences. The revision group seeks merely to accomplish physical realizability with the least practical repercussion in the balance of the design.

When the prototypes are to serve an experimental purpose, greater freedom in revision is permissible, but only for good cause and with economic justification. Change for change's sake is tantamount to technical disaster.

Promising new ideas should be recognized, even rewarded where appropriate, and filed for possible future use when the next generation of the product is to be designed.

This is the first full-scale opportunity to check the concepts of the design in the actual transition to physical realization. The project team seeking to uncover every flaw in the design, should work closely with the shop technicians assigned to the actual work of fabrication. It is also the testing ground for uncovering problems of producibility; they will stand out as the experimental fabrication progresses, and they should be noted in great detail, because later they must be faced so that they will not return to haunt the project under the vastly more complex situation of full-scale production. This is particularly a time when the project team should be looking at the design principally from the point of view of the producer, vitally concerned with the ways of simplifying the production processes and of reducing the cost of manufacture.

For the designer the production of the first prototype is a time of heightened interest–almost excitement. It is a time for feeling the joy and pain of creation, when the ideas, conceived in the mind and nurtured in the abstract, issue into the world of physical reality; when the archetype materializes in the prototype.

PRODUCT TEST PROGRAM—STEP 7

While the fabrication of the prototype is under way, the test program is readied. Test programs can be enormously expensive, and if improperly planned, yield only meager evidence for or against the design, or scant information on which to base suitable revisions. In general, the comments already made in Chapter 5 about experimental work and testing apply at this point also.

The prototype is a first approximation of the product which will be put in the hands of the consumer. Whereas the project team was mainly producer-oriented while the prototype was being fabricated, their point of view changes; they now become much more consumer-oriented. A central question becomes: how well will this product perform for the consumer?

ANALYSIS AND PREDICTION—STEP 8

With the notes and records of the experimental construction and the data and other general observations of the test program, preparation for revision or redesign can begin.

An accurate cost analysis can be made which will update the last one. If the cost is still satisfactory, then other considerations will draw the attention of the project team. If the estimated production cost is too high, which is frequently the case, then a major program of cost reduction must be mounted as a basis for subsequent redesign. Some of the means by which cost reduction may be accomplished are: simplifying the design, relaxing tight tolerances, easing some of the less-critical performance specifications, using lower cost materials, and substituting cheaper production processes. If the best achievements of the cost reduction analysis are definitely inadequate to bring the estimated production cost into competitive alignment, management will again face the decision of ordering the project abandoned, or of continuing it on a probationary basis until the evidence becomes more conclusive.

Other problems bearing on production will need penetrating analyses, such as assembly problems, special fabricating problems, general suitability for the manufacturing facilities of the company, special packaging or warehouse problems, problems involving hazards to personnel, and so on. Most of these will have been considered before, but now they can be reviewed in the light of more experience.

From the test data it becomes possible to make definitive statements about some aspects of performance and to make predictions about others. If the performance, observed or predicted from the test results, is not adequate, then the various problems which are posed in planning its improvement must be attacked. Some of the problems can be resolved by analysis. Others will not be amenable to paper and pencil solutions, but will require development programs in the experimental laboratories. Most of the problems will best be solved by a judicious combination of analysis and experimentation.

REDESIGN–STEP 9

The analysis and predictions of performance, that are the prelude to redesign, are analogous to the preliminary design, which prepared the over-all concepts for the detailed design. If the experimental construction and the test program have not dealt too harshly with the original design, the work of redesign may be principally that of minor revision. If major flaws and shortcomings have been exposed, then the work of redesign may reach major proportions, and entirely new concepts may have to be sought for major components and even for subsystems.

The overall concept for the system may prove, beyond the hope of rescue, to have failed. A completely new design may virtually be dictated; such is the risk of design. Usually there are warnings along the way, but that design leader who is insensitive to danger signals may find himself ultimately confronting disaster. Then, like the pitcher on the mound, whose pitching has not matched his promise, he is quietly retired to the side lines.

Revisions in design, be they major or minor, always threaten the integrity of the whole design. So intricate is the pattern that has been woven, so interrelated are the parts of a system, that a seemingly innocuous change may produce a many-stranded chain of accommodating revisions which, diverging in unsuspecting ways, may jar the whole design with its impact, like the messenger who, lacking a nail in the shoe of his horse, started a chain of events that lost the kingdom. As an illustration, suppose a gear box is bolted to the frame of a machine. It may be that one of the bolts must be larger because shear failures were encountered in the tests. But a larger bolt requires a larger nut, and even when the latter is under-sized it still interferes with one of the gears. Accordingly the gear box is made slightly longer to allow for additional clearance, but now the final drive to the machine must be altered, and so the changes go on.

It is clear that the consequences of each revision must be anticipated with the greatest of care. As in prior steps of design we will prefer to conceive several concepts of possible solutions for each design revision. With alternative solutions at hand we need a criterion of selection to sort out the most suitable one. The details of this process are deferred to Chapter 9, "Decision Processes in Design," but it is worth noting here a modification of the decision criterion, appropriate for revisions. The usual criterion in making critical decisions in detailed design, when advantages for the several alternatives are more or less equivalent, is the cost of effecting a physically realizable design. Essentially, this remains the basis of the criterion; but now the cost is principally dependent on the number of ancillary revisions occasioned by the primary one. Hence the criterion can be stated: when advantages are equivalent, select the alternative which, while solving the problems of the revision, will be most compatible with the whole design, that is, require the least secondary changes.

SUMMARY OF THE DETAILED DESIGN PHASE

We have seen that the detailed design, involving large commitments for design work, requires careful preparation of capital budgets and time schedules. This is the first step. Top-management in the light of these estimates must decide whether to continue with the design project. If the decision is favorable, then a project organization must be developed.

The second and third steps involving the overall designs of subsystems and components are similar in many ways to the preliminary design. In the fourth step, the detailed design of parts is undertaken, and followed in the fifth step by the preparation of assemblies for the components and subsystems.

In the sixth and seventh steps the prototype is constructed and tested. The difficulties encountered in both of the operations, constructing and testing, become the subjects of analysis in the eighth step. Also, performance is predicted under conditions of customers' operations, and any short-comings, evident or anticipated, are included in the difficulties.

The final step is the making of revisions. A major concern is to affect the design as a whole as little as possible, for small revisions can start a chain of consequences which could destroy the integrity of the design.

Finally, the iterative character of design work should be noted. After the revisions have been made in the redesign step, construction of new prototypes and subsequent testing may follow, again leading to further revisions. A successful project is, however, highly convergent so that only a few iterations are required to reach a final solution. The high rate of convergence stems from the high confidence levels which are required in critical decisions (see Chapter 9).

chapter

7

THE DESIGN PROCESS

Engineering design is a specialized process of problem solving. Although it has its own peculiar way, suited to a technological pattern, its process resembles that of problem solving in general.

THE GENERAL PROCESS OF SOLVING PROBLEMS

Many kinds of words have been used to define the major steps in problem solving. One writer speaks of *diagnosis, attack, scientific method,* and *art.** Another writer originally listed these features: *define, search, evaluate,* and *select.*† Psychologists, in writing about creative thought in connection with problem solving, have categorized the elements of *preparation, illumination,* and *verification.*‡ Sometimes the last element is called *revision.* Logically *revision* might be added to the three elements above for solving more complicated problems in which several iterations may be required for their resolution.

When we examine the ideas behind the words, we find substantial, although not complete, agreement. At the first stage an effort is made to understand the problem. Von Fange (*loc. cit.*) has defined a problem as a perplexing situation. Essentially then, the effort is to understand what it is that is perplexing in the situation. Information about the perplexing

---

* Edward Hodnett, *The Art of Problem Solving* (New York: Harper and Brothers, 1955).

† Eugene Von Fange, *Professional Creativity* (Englewood Cliffs, N. J.: Prentice Hall, Inc., 1959).

‡ Robert S. Woodworth, *Experimental Psychology* (New York: Henry Holt and Co., 1938).

factors in the situation is needed and is sought at various sources. At this first stage there is complete agreement: diagnose, define, prepare; all imply an *understanding* of the problem and an explicit statement of the goals which the problem-solver wishes to attain.

There is also agreement about the second stage—solutions exist and if we are imaginative and creative we ought to find a number of alternative solutions. Somehow, under certain favorable conditions the mind can synthesize plausible solutions. These foregoing ideas seem to fit the intended definitions of each of the following: attack, search, and illumination.

The third stage is directed toward judging the validity of the solution relative to goals that were defined, and, if there are alternatives, selecting the most suitable one. At this point it appears to be essential to give the mental images and impressions of the solution a more formal expression. The unexpressed ideas, unclothed in verbalism or symbolism, seem to be too nebulous to test even mentally for validity. The procedure, when it is overt, is to state the solution as a testable hypothesis or mind-model. In this form its concordance with the external world can be judged: first, by referring and comparing it with one's own experience, with the experience of others, and with recorded knowledge; second, by analytical or logical manipulation and by mental or analytical exploration of the consequences of action based on the proposed solution; or third, by actual experimentation. Finally, among the valid solutions, the one which appears to be best is selected. These ideas seem to be the substantial implications of the terms: scientific method and art, evaluate and select, and verification.

Drawing together the comments about problem solving, we see that there is some consensus that the process includes at least three stages: the first is an analysis of the situation in which the problem is embedded; the second is a synthesis of possible solutions; the third is an evaluation of the solutions and, if there are acceptable ones, a decision on which one is best. To these three may be added a fourth stage: revision, which improves the chosen solution.

A STATEMENT OF THE DESIGN PROCESS

In the *morphology* we saw that the vertical structure of engineering design was a skeleton around which the design project could be planned, organized, and evolved. We now point out that engineering design has a horizontal structure as well. We find the horizontal structure, sometimes in full, sometimes only in part, in every step of the morphology as we move down its vertical structure from the needs analysis of the feasibility study to the final revision step in the detailed design. Each of these steps possesses in a rather complete form a typical sequence of operations. It is this typical sequence which we call the *design process*. It is distinctively a process for solving the problems of engineering design, just as the scientific method is a process for solving the problems of research. Since every step in the morphology poses a particular problem which has to be solved, it is clear that the design process should appear in every step.

⊣ The design process describes the gathering, handling, and creative organizing of information relevant to the problem situation; it prescribes the derivation of decisions which are optimized, communicated, and tested or otherwise evaluated; it has an iterative character, for often, in the doing, new information becomes available or new insights are gained which require the repetition of earlier operations. Some of the operations are qualitatively logical in character, like reasoning from verbal propositions; some are based on subjective evaluations, as in comparing or combining unlike values; many are amenable to quantitative analysis and to computer applications, as in optimizing an analytically formulated representation of a problem solution. For the most part the techniques associated with each operation in the design process are of such great generality that their usefulness is not limited to any particular step.

The design process resembles the general process of problem solving in the main features, but it uses sharper, and for the most part, more analytical tools, which have been especially shaped and sharpened for the problems of engineering design. It carries the process through *analysis, synthesis,* and *evaluation and decision,* and extends it into the realms of *optimization,* ✝ *revision,* and *implementation.*

THE ANALYSIS OF THE PROBLEM SITUATION

Problems seldom come ready-made with a fine, clear statement of the factors involved and a sprinkling of well-marked clues to indicate the one correct solution. Indeed, it is usually unclear whether there is a single problem or several, and, if there are several, what they are. The designer is presented, not with a problem, but with a problem situation, a situation which may have many perplexing elements interrelated in complicated and obscure patterns. It is out of this milieu of perplexity that clear definitions of the relevant problems must be drawn. We use the plural, because more often than not there will be more than one problem; we qualify the statement with relevant, because many problems which inhere in the situation are immaterial to our purpose.

We equate problems with difficulties which, existing in the situation, obstruct the approach to our goals. More accurately, difficulties are the obstructing elements which we perceive in the situation; problems are the questions which we ask when we reflect on how to overcome the difficulties. Except for the very simple situations, we cannot pose the problems until we have uncovered the difficulties; we cannot uncover the difficulties until we have clarified our goals in relation to the situation to which we are attending.

A *goal* is the end to which a design tends.* Some activities, for example industrial research, can be directed toward general and broadly defined

---

* Definition, *Webster's New International Dictionary, Unabridged,* Second Edition, 1951.

goals, but in engineering design, goals must be as specific as we can possibly make them; and they must be made explicit so that they are the common property of the designer, his supervisor, and any others who are concerned with the immediate endeavor. Goals are never developed in a vacuum; they are conditioned by larger objectives. For instance, in a problem situation involving excessive power to drive a particular component, the goal might be to reduce friction, or to reduce mass, or to reduce the load, depending on the larger goals which apply to the component.

When we work with a problem situation we usually find that we do not know enough about the factors that compose it. We try to bring our goals into focus, although even these may be revised in light of future evidence. We explore our knowledge and our ignorance in the situation as it pertains to the goals, and identify the kind of information we need and the sources whence we might obtain it. Information, we must recognize, is an economic commodity. It has a cost; and the quantity that we need, assuming that we have not erred in fixing the kind we need, is the amount we require for an *understanding* of what we judge to be the relevant factors.

As we gain understanding of the problem situation, we are enabled to see the actual difficulties, and we can begin to ask the proper questions. At first the questions are of the who? what? where? when? variety that serves to isolate the important factors. Then they become more of the how? why? kind, suited to clarify the causal and correlative relations. The questions suggest additional information to be obtained, and they demand particular attention to the organization of the information in order to extract the maximum meaning.

The random questions can finally be fitted together in a pattern which constitutes a *statement of the problem*. The statement makes clear what goals are to be achieved, what difficulties must be overcome, what resources are available, what constraints will circumscribe any acceptable solution, and finally, what criterion should be used to judge the goodness of a possible solution. The preparation of such a statement can only come after a substantial understanding of the problem situation has been achieved.

SYNTHESIS OF SOLUTIONS

With the problem statement before us we can begin the search for solutions. A *solution* is a synthesis of component elements which hurdles the obstructing difficulties and, neither exceeding the available resources nor encroaching on the limits set by the constraints, accomplishes the prescribed goals. What are and whence come the component elements? For the most part they are stored in our memory; we add to the store as our experience widens and as our ability to see and hear the potentially useful sharpens. The elements may be of ideas or of physical things. What enables us to draw from the warehouse of our experience just the right set of elements, and to put them into just the right combination so that they have a sense of fitting the situation, we do not know, since no definite formula exists.

There is always more than one solution to a problem, and we seek out as many as we can within the limit of alloted time. These we carry to the next step in the design process.

EVALUATION AND DECISION

Agile as the mind may be in synthesizing solutions, it usually fails in the effort of visualizing how a particular solution would fit in a multidimensional situation varying in time. As we have already pointed out (Chapter 5) it is for this reason that the solutions must be given symbolic or verbal forms so that they can be manipulated by the rules of logic and mathematics. In this manner we can test the solution in the abstract against the spectrum of requirements in the situation and thereby arrive at an evaluation. In doing so we will use measures of performance, some objective and some subjective. Having the evaluations, we make the decision of which solution to adopt by taking account of the possibility that any particular solution might turn out unfavorably (see Chapter 9, "Decision Processes in Design").

OPTIMIZATION

The solution, favored by the decision, is by no means ready for use. We have now to refine it. For the early analyses a general version of the solution was good enough, since it was necessary for the major features only of the solution concept to emerge. But in this operation we wish to bring the concept to a theoretical level of perfection. How this is done is the subject of Chapter 11, "Techniques of Optimization."

REVISION

In engineering design every solution must be tested if there is any reasonable doubt about its being satisfactory. The tests may reveal flaws that do not, however, discredit the solution as a whole. From the test, data projections and predictions about the quality of the solution may be inferred, and these may indicate other possible flaws. We have discussed at some length in Chapter 5 the operation of revision as it appears in detailed design; here also the solution is similarly revised, the process often being iterated, until the flaws have been reduced, and the solution, while complying with the constraints and employing no more than the available resources, is able to reach the goals.

IMPLEMENTATION

Only the very minor solutions are solely for personal consideration in engineering design. They can, perhaps, be left in rough form, for no one else will have to judge their merits. But important solutions pass beyond our personal sphere. They must be communicated. Communication is often a perilous adventure, beset with semantic pitfalls and strewn with the pages of misunderstood proposals and solutions, discarded and dead, but it must be essayed; for there is no other way in a design project, except for occasional alternatives, to implement the solution.

THE PROCESSES OF DESIGN AND RESEARCH

Research, development, and design are often so intermingled in the language of present-day technology that disentangling them can be very difficult. All three are concerned with problem solving. In each case the problem is embedded in a problem situation, and the first task is to make clear the immediate goals. As before, the goals are oriented by the overall objectives, but the degree to which the goals are dictated is not the same for each of the functions.

In a general way, the object of an industrial research program is to find new elements of technology which will be useful to the firm sooner or later. The probability of finding some particular kind of element which management might especially want is rather low; but the probability that some other new element, not originally anticipated, but nonetheless potentially useful, might be discovered in the process is reasonably high. It is somewhat like hunting for pearls and ending up with an oyster stew. Indeed the odds are favorable enough for a satisfactory payoff over the long term, so that enlightened management, whose firms can afford the investment, are willing to gamble heavily on industrial research. In a way, research is opportunistic. The exploration of one problem situation is not so much to find a particular kind of solution as to find clues which lead in promising directions. Industrial research differs from pure research principally in that the problem situations in the former are dictated by the research program, while in the latter even the problem situation is not imposed and the area of inquiry is only loosely defined.

The immediate goals of industrial research are broad and fluid, the researcher being charged only with the mission of searching for potentially useful elements within the constraints of a problem situation. By contrast, not only is the problem situation of design fixed by the design project, but the goals that the solution is to achieve are strictly attuned to the goals which were set one step higher in that part of the design project which contains the present problem. The latter goals are likewise aligned to superior ones, and so on until the original overall objectives of the design project are reached. Development work is intermediate between the two others, although its goals are much more tightly bound to a superior objective than research goals.

The operational procedure is similar in principle for the three functions, although there will usually be large differences in details of method and in the tools employed. As information about the problem situation is acquired and we learn more about the controlling factors, we are enabled to isolate the difficulties and frame the problem. It is at the point when we begin the synthesis of solutions that we encounter another major difference. In research, the outcome of synthesis is one or more alternative hypotheses; in design, it is one or more alternative design concepts. It is true that both outcomes are concepts, but the hypothesis of research is a generalization, while the concept in design is a specialization. Research is directed toward obtaining a class of answers; design, toward a specific answer. The end product of research is a finding which will be true in many situations; of design, a piece of hardware. Research proceeds from the abstract to the general; design from the abstract to the concrete. Research provides new technical ideas for design (and also for industrial operations) which are not limited to a particular design. Again, development is intermediate, mixing the experimental work of research with the single mindedness of design, and ending with some new physical element which can be incorporated in various designs.

Whether hypothesis or design concept, the idea must be formulated for mathematical or logical manipulation, and its implications explored under varying circumstances. It is evaluated, and the hypothesis of research, which predicts particular consequences under certain circumstances, is tested. If the tests reveal the predicted consequences, the hypothesis is accepted as a useful explanation of a segment of nature's behavior; if not, the hypothesis is revised or an alternative is tested. If all methods fail, then that particular effort in research is abandoned and other problems in the problem situation are investigated. In the case of design, the most advantageous solution is selected. The basic question is not whether the concept is a useful explanation, but whether it is physically realizable. When analysis or testing, if necessary, reveals that this is not so, then it is revised, or another alternative is substituted. Unlike research, some acceptable solution must be found; failure is disaster.

We shall make one final comment. The resemblance between the horizontal structure and the vertical is not accidental; for the design process deals with the solution of subordinate problems, while the morphology bears on the solution of the project as a whole.

ANALYSIS OF

NEEDS AND ACTIVITY

The design process prescribes setting goals and evolving a problem statement. But, in large and confused problem situations, these can be difficult tasks. The needs analysis comprises an assortment of techniques which, concerned, as they are, with the needs or goals that the system (or any subdivision thereof) is required to satisfy, provides the basis for defining the overall objectives of the design project. Similarly, the activity analysis, which is essentially a study of the boundary conditions of the system, enables us to derive the problem statement for the whole project, or, when we wish, for its subdivisions.

NEEDS ANALYSIS—RESOLVING THE PROBLEM SITUATION

The needs analysis, we recall, is the first step in the feasibility study. The performing of the needs analysis is itself an act of solving a problem. Therefore the presentation will follow the format which was set forth for the design process. Although the design process is better attuned to problems more immediately involving the design of hardware, its application here is appropriate to illustrate the design process, and at the same time to allow us to fulfill our primary purpose, that of presenting the needs analysis. We shall do the same later for the activity analysis.

We assume that we have been given a primitive statement of needs. By primitive we mean that the statement represents opinion based mainly on casual observations, but unsupported by organized evidence. Such opinions are valuable as starting points when they come from people who have had the opportunity and have the ability to make observations and to temper them with considered judgment. Sales people, constantly feeling the pulse of the market, often have ideas about needs which are worthy of examination; technical personnel, loosing their thoughts on imaginative excursions, come upon ideas that seem suited tó the market. Bright, new ideas, translatable into primitive statements of need can come from many sources, and some will be worth the expense of preliminary exploration.

The primitive statement suggests the problem situation which might, for example, be thought of as an alleged need, presented in primitive form, ascribed to various kinds of potential customers who might seek the proposed product in some undefined market place, conditioned by unevaluated competitive influences, and subject to unidentified social, economic, and political pressures. We set the goal for the needs analysis, namely to determine the effective needs which the system should satisfy. Effective needs we will define as those which have an existence in the market place, by virtue of consumers' willingness and ability to acquire the means for their satisfaction. Consumers, we note, can be of various types: the public at large, some certain part of the population, industries, or the many agencies of the government.

We face many difficulties in reaching the above-stated goal. In the first place we must avoid the hazard of assigning to consumers the needs we feel they ought to have, for we are likely to be biased by what we think is possible in the technology. In the second place, what consumers say they want may be surprisingly different from what they will buy later when the product becomes available. Error in judging the effective needs will usually cause a much greater financial loss than failure to produce a workable design. The needs we want to determine are the effective ones that will exist when the product is ready for the market, many months away. We have many questions to ask. How will consumers' tastes change? What will competitors offer? What will be the economic climate? What legislation may be enacted that might influence the use of the product? How can we classify consumers into groups? How can we take account of their different spending habits, economic positions, social behaviors, and so on? The difficulties are due largely to our lack of market information and current trends, partly because we are unable to make reliable estimates of future situations, and, to a very large extent, because we do not yet have a physical product.

The precise formulation of the problem statement will, of course, depend on the nature of the product and the sector of the economy to be served. But in a general way it will be as follows: to develop what appear to be the effective needs which the system or device must be able to satisfy, and to adduce enough organized supporting evidence to warrant a strong conviction that, if a physically realizable and economically worthwhile design can be executed, the result will be a marketable commodity. To elaborate the problem statement further, we wish to detail the needs precisely in terms of the ways in which the consumer will use the product. We wish to know who the consumers will be and how they should be categorized. If each category or segment has particular and distinguishing characteristics we wish to know how these will be reflected in the manner of use. We will need to know the dimensions of the whole market and of each segment in order to judge the relative importance of the individual items in the set of needs. We will wish to know the time-dependent characteristics of the market, that is, the important trends and their effects on each market segment, so that we can make adjustments among the items of need to compensate for anticipated changes.

In the context of the needs analysis, we will define a *solution* as a plan of action for determining the unknown elements specified in the problem statement. Actual, possible plans will hinge so much on the particular situation that detailed development is not feasible here. In a general way, the approaches which are possible are of two kinds: one is an appeal to a sort of experimental introspection, the other, to the market place and the consumer. The plan to adopt will include some mixture of the two approaches, and alternative solution concepts will differ in the mixture and in the choice of particular applications of the two approaches.

The first approach we will be required to use often. Whenever we contemplate the plausibility of a particular design concept for some object, we will have to try to visualize it as if it actually existed and being used, and then to mirror in the mind what the consequences of the use might be. This mode of visualization, conducting experiments in the mind, is an important talent for a designer to cultivate. We will now imagine some kind of shape or form without detail which we will focus in our mind's eye, as if we were trying to satisfy the needs in the primitive statement. After carrying on some of this kind of introspection we may wish to make a crude mock-up of the imagined shape and simultaneously experiment physically and introspectively. Such testing, combining physical and introspective efforts, can be extended to include people roughly representative of supposed categories of consumers.

If this approach were pushed to its ultimate conclusion, the mock-up would eventually become the end product, and, in effect, the design would have been executed by development work. For simple products this is sometimes feasible. For complicated products, development work is used whenever necessary to support paper-and-pencil design, bearing in mind that it is usually much higher in cost. Here, the mock-up can be refined in physical shape without attempting any operating detail to increase the impression of reality, while the user is asked to imagine that the mock-up is performing functions clearly explained to him by words and pictures.

In a manner similar to that described in the foregoing, the primitive statement of needs is matched with the experimental situation and revised to make a better fit. At this stage of the work, collaboration with an industrial designer or a human factors specialist may be very helpful. An illustration taken from a commercial situation will show the essential role of the needs analysis. We assume the primitive statement: "A refrigerator is needed which can deliver ice cubes automatically as well as performing the usual household functions such as ——." In Crisp's Marketing Research*, the author relates ". . . the makers of Servel refrigerators in 1953

---

*See Richard D. Crisp, *Marketing Research* (New York: McGraw-Hill, 1957), pp. 55–56.

introduced a new model which made ice cubes automatically, eliminating the need for trays . . . Was this development destined to revolutionize refrigerators . . . ? Consumer checks by a competitor indicated reaction . . . mixed to negative. Objections were . . . that the ice-making mechanism took up so much space that it reduced the frozen food capacity . . . which was more important to housewives . . . ." Clearly, this was a costly venture which might have been reconsidered if a thorough needs analysis had been performed, before any serious design commitments were made.

A marketing research specialist should be enlisted to help plan and to execute the research. There are many techniques (*loc. cit.*) available from which plans can be fashioned, although the lack of a final product is a severe handicap which requires great ingenuity to overcome. Indeed, the several possible alternative plans may be premised on different schemes of substitutes for the product. For example, some existing product, closest in nature to the proposed device, might be adapted for the purpose by appropriately reshaping its external form to comply with some of the preliminary concepts and to serve also to destroy its original identity so that possible recognition by the user will not affect the outcomes. Such functions as are available and appropriate to the test can be preserved and the remaining ones can be described by pictures and charts. In general, the user should be presented with two such adaptations, differing with respect to some of the functions. By getting him to concentrate, obstensibly on the differences, a skillful interviewer can extract much unbiased information about the general concept.

We should note that marketing research specialists are well informed of consumer interviewing techniques, but are sometimes not well prepared in the design of statistical experiments. If a plan of any consequence in size is contemplated, we will have to tend to the latter consideration, or else include a statistician on the team. Finally, marketing research is expensive and anything larger than an exploratory plan at this early stage in the design should be considered cautiously.

We have touched very briefly on marketing research; most of the questions posed in the problem statement are left untreated. To explore them would take us too far afield. They belong to the vast literature of marketing research.*

In the area of very large equipment and complex systems, the consumer is usually much more accessible and the complicating problems of dealing with an amorphous market are avoided. However, the needs analysis must be carried through even more diligently, for it will be more complicated in form and more exacting in sharpness of definition. Usually the customer

---

* See the section on Market Research and Bibliography in John H. Perry, Editor-in-Chief, *Chemical Business Handbook* (New York: McGraw-Hill Book Company, 1954). See also Wales and Ferber, *Bibliography on Marketing Research* (Chicago: American Marketing Association, 1956).

supplies the primitive statement of need, sometimes considerably refined. The needs must be thoroughly explored to establish their validity bearing in mind the long lapse before the end product can be delivered. A design project, abandoned after it has progressed far toward completion because the customer does not now want what he had claimed he wanted originally, is just as hurtful as one abandoned for technical reasons. In either case technical talent and supervision, scarce and costly resources, which could have been employed on work with future potential, have been wasted, even though the customer pays for the aborted design effort when terminated at his request.

ACTIVITY ANALYSIS—THE PROBLEM SITUATION

The activity analysis continues the effort, started in the needs analysis, of constructing the overall problem statement. However, the problem situation has shifted, the center of the area being the boundary between a possible system and the enveloping environment. The content of the problem situation derives from the unknown circumstances to which any proposed system must be accommodated. For example, the problem situation might appear as the search for a suitable system which could satisfy some well-defined needs; but the resources required to operate the system are unknown with respect to kind, quantity, or availability; the constraints which the social, economic, and political environment will impose on the system are undetermined, and the methods or measures by which to evaluate proposed systems are not established.

The goal of the activity analysis is the determination of the boundaries and the boundary conditions which will apply to any proposed system, and with which the system must accord before it may be considered as a possible solution. The difficulties which deter us are, as usual, informational, although much of the information obtained for the needs analysis will be useful here. We may have to know more about customer's value judgments, their facilities or resources which would be available for operating the system, laws or regulations that might apply to systems of this type, and so on.

The general problem of the activity analysis is the establishment of a good plan for achieving its stated goals, namely the establishment in detail of the boundaries and boundary conditions of the system. The activity analysis prescribes a general mode of attack based on analyzing the inputs and the demanded outputs of a system whose form is unknown. This mode of attack is the general strategy. The specific problem of the activity analysis is the implementation of the strategy with the proper tactics, that is, with a detailed plan suited to the problem situation. Here, we will present the strategy; the tactics we must leave to the ingenuity of the designer and the exigencies of the particular situation.

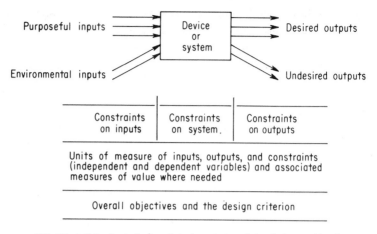

FIG. 8.1 Activity Analysis. (Leads to formulation of the design problem.)

ACTIVITY ANALYSIS—THE GENERAL PLAN

The general plan of the activity analysis is indicated in Figure 8.1 and elaborated in the outline below. Although the steps are shown consecutively, there may be much iteration among them.

(1) The desired outputs of the system are derived from the effective needs of the consumer. The language of the outputs should be more precise than that of the needs, and should reflect what the system does or provides in response to the eliciting needs.

(2) The undesired outputs of the system are deduced. It seems almost inevitable that undesired outputs accompany the production of those desired. A refrigerator extracts heat to keep food fresh; simultaneously it extracts moisture which spoils the flavor. A lamp produces the light to read by; at the same time the heat that it radiates makes us uncomfortable.

(3) The inputs, which the system will transform into outputs, are deduced. If the system delivers mechanical energy, we know that fuel or energy must be an input. We can classify the inputs into five categories:

(a) physical, such as energy, materials, and motion;
(b) human, such as effort, control, and mere presence;
(c) informational, such as error signals, coded data, and instrumental controls;
(d) economic, such as the costs of operation, maintenance, and depreciation;
(e) environmental, such as heat, shock, and moisture.

(4) The constraints which will apply to both outputs and inputs are determined. These will usually take the form of specifications, limits, tolerances and other definitions of acceptable or limiting qualities. Every output, desired or undesired, every input, purposive or incidental, should be considered, and if possible, set into its proper bounds as required for the

system to be compatible with its purpose, its environment, and the consequences of its use (e.g. safety, aesthetics, and convenience).

(5) The constraints on the system itself are considered along with any design parameters that are now evident. The constraints may be on size or weight or speed or other attributes of the system. Many of the attributes, so constrained, will be design parameters of the system.

(6) The appropriate measures of value for the outputs and inputs and for the design parameters are set out. By doing so, we are able to quantify the analysis. In many cases the assignment of measures of value will be obvious, as in using pounds to measure the weight of the system, but in other cases it will require great ingenuity, and in still others it will remain intangible. For example, it is not easy to assign a proper meaningful measure of value to safety, although often it can be done.

(7) The criteria for measuring the goodness of proposed systems are developed from appropriate relationships among the variables, namely the inputs, outputs, and design parameters. Some of the more useful criteria, involving measurable variables, will be in quantified form. In general, a criterion expresses the amount of the output functions that can be realized from various amounts of input resources.

ACTIVITY ANALYSIS—AN EXAMPLE

The meticulous performance of an activity analysis is a task of some magnitude. We shall illustrate a very simple one here; but, because of lack of space, it will be brief and cursory, serving to exemplify the outlined procedure only rather than to display a model of performance.

The effective need (as developed in the needs analysis):–to be able to read continuously, while in operation, the performance of an automobile in respect to fuel economy.

Desired output:–a display on a suitable scale of miles vs. fuel consumption.

Undesired outputs or effects:–complicating the appearance of the dash board; adding resistance to flow of fuel; increasing the output requirements of the fuel pump.

Purposeful inputs, physical:–fuel passing through the metering device; additional energy to fuel pump; *human and informational*: none of particular consequence or relevance; *economic*:–amortization cost of the device and its installation.

Incidental inputs, environmental:–road shock, engine vibration, higher than ambient temperature.

Constraints, outputs:–readings should be able to range within specified lowest and highest values; the indication should be sensitive to an increment of change in performance not less than a certain specified minimum.

Constraints, inputs:–the lowest fuel rate able to cause a response must not exceed a maximum limit; the greatest pressure drop must not exceed a maximum limit.

Constraints on the device:–installation on any automobile should not exceed a prescribed degree of difficulty; the size of the device should be no greater than a given maximum; the cost should not exceed a certain amount.

Measures of value and design parameters:–fuel consumption to be measured in gallons per hour; rate of travel in miles per hour; amortization cost in dollars per year; fuel cost in dollars per year; cost of device in dollars; installation in dollars; sensitivity in percentage of total range; area required on the dash board in inches squared.

Criteria:–the ratio of fuel savings to amortization cost; the ratio of the cost of installation to the cost of the device; the ratio of the indicated performance to actual performance; the length of time required to save in fuel the equivalent of the cost of the device by operating the automobile more efficiently when the performance is measured. With these results before us we can begin to insert tentatively acceptable values where needed, and start constructing the problem statement for the design project, remembering that tentative results are subject to revisions as the study proceeds and iterations are made.

PRODUCT DEVELOPMENT PROGRAMS

Many firms recognize new product development as the key to their survival. The exploration of possible new products must be a continuing one; for, as is well known, only a fraction of the ideas, which at first seem good, blossom into commercial success. The cost of separating the successes from the failures is large; often it is very large because the project is not abandoned until the product is ready for production. When the failure occurs in the market place, the monetary loss is still greater, and there is an additional loss in prestige; the latter may be even more damaging than the money loss. It is my personal belief that much money and disappointment could be saved in industry by executing well planned needs and activity analyses, and thereby revealing early the potential failures.

DECISION PROCESSES IN DESIGN

Making good decisions is man's most difficult and crucial task. It lies at the heart of all human problems. It determines the direction in which human effort will be directed. If good decisions are made, man moves closer to his aspirations; if the decisions are poor, his goals recede. Good decisions are based on the immediate evidence of one's senses, the accumulated experience of one's lifetime, the intuitive feeling for what is proper and fitting, and the recorded wisdom of civilization. The evidence must be brought to bear upon the feasible alternatives which the individual perceives, thereby enabling him to single out from the plurality the one that appears likely to be the best means of attaining the desired ends. In this chapter we wish to see how the problem of making decisions arises in design; how evidence is formulated and used; which factors, inherent to the process of design, have a critical influence; and finally, which procedures and criteria are useful in making a decision.

THE NATURE OF A DECISION

Not all decisions that arise in the course of a design project are equally important. There are innumerable minute to minute decisions to be made whose influence on the design is relatively inconsequential. Other decisions, however, are critical in that they have a major impact on the design. Decision situations that are particularly critical as a class are those which arise after a design problem, occurring at any level in the design, has been studied and a number of plausible solutions have been developed. Which solution to adopt is a critical question, for its answer affects the form and substance of the design. The following is concerned only with the class of critical design decisions.

We assume that we have available a set of alternative plausible solutions. Each solution has associated with it sundry advantages and benefits which are expected to accrue if it is adopted. However, each solution, implying a particular course of design action, leads to various consequences or difficulties which may be more or less easy to overcome. Thus, the three elements that concern us in critical decision making, as it appears in the design process, are the alternatives, the benefits, and the difficulties of implementation. To help in resolving the issue, we seek and apply relevant evidence.

Clearly, we should like to adopt, other things being equal, that alternative solution from which we should derive the greatest advantages and benefits. In principle we can make such a distinction between the alternatives subject to the problems of making value measurements. Let the whole set of possible advantages be $(V_1 \ldots V_m)$. Among these there will be some that are substantially the same for all alternatives. These will not add to the ability to distinguish; therefore they can be omitted as immaterial. Let the set of available alternatives be $A_1 \ldots A_n$. Each alternative will presumably have some kind of a rating resulting from a value judgment. We can tabulate the set of ratings V_{ij} in the form of a matrix.

$$
\begin{array}{c|ccc}
 & A_1 \ldots A_n \\
\hline
V_1 & V_{11} \ldots V_{1n} \\
\cdot & \cdot \quad \cdot \\
\cdot & \cdot \quad \cdot \\
\cdot & \cdot \quad \cdot \\
V_m & \cdot \ldots V_{mn}
\end{array}
$$

Hypothetically, that alternative which possesses the most favorable subset of ratings would be selected as the successful contender in the list. However, it may be a difficult solution to implement. This brings us face to face with the question how to compare a solution that exhibits very favorable benefits, but appears to be difficult to apply, with one that is less desirable from the standpoint of benefits, but is relatively easy to realize.

The difficulties with which we are here concerned spring primarily from uncertainties about physical realizability. Questions about economic worthwhileness, financial feasibility, social consequences, political effects, and possible interrelations with other engineering systems, can be relegated to the set of relevant advantages and benefits. The question of physical realizability stands apart as the core of design activity. Particularly, we are interested in the ease with which physical realizability can be attained. Hereafter we will refer to this as *tractability*.

A HYPOTHESIS ABOUT PHYSICAL REALIZABILITY

Physical realizability is not a simple and primitive concept. It depends on an interrelationship between several factors. In order to make the concept useful for decision making we must develop a theory of physical realizability that explicates the effect of the underlying factors. To this end we shall set out two hypotheses: the first will allow us to develop the theory; the second will suggest which of the two criteria implied by the theory it is proper to use in a given design situation.

Hypothesis I: Virtually any solution, even a very difficult one, provided it is physically permissable (e.g., not a perpetual motion machine), can be carried through to a physically realizable design if a sufficiently large amount of money is appropriated and an indefinite amount of design time allowed. If the budget of time and money is limited, then whether or not the design is realizable becomes uncertain. The greater the limitation, the more uncertainty it raises.

We assert that experience with complex design projects substantially supports this hypothesis. It is to be noted that the hypothesis does not state that it is proper, economical, or practical to allow excessive budgets for design.

BELIEF AND UNCERTAINTY IN DECISION MAKING

The foregoing hypothesis indicates that the prospect of achieving a design that can be realized physically depends on two general factors—namely, cost as measured in time and money which will be allowed for the particular piece of design work, and the evidence that a physically realizable design can be accomplished. We consider the latter factor. Belief that the particular design task can be accomplished successfully depends on the amount of favorable evidence. Part of the task of design consists in seeking and gathering information about whether and how the design can be accomplished. As we learn more about how to achieve the design, we at the same time obtain favorable evidence to support a stronger belief in its ultimate success. As our belief (or confidence) in the physical realizability of the particular concept is strengthened, we are more inclined to select it, especially if the concomitant advantages are comparable to the alternatives.

There is a subtle distinction to be made between two kinds of decision situations. Generally, a decision hinges on some future event. We gather evidence to indicate whether this future event shall transpire, but the gathering of the evidence usually has no effect on the occurrence of the event. Thus, the evidence we collect now about next week's weather will not affect the actual weather. In a design situation, however, the evidence we collect has an effect on the future event by showing how it can be brought to a successful conclusion.

What kind of evidence do we gather to enhance our belief that the concept can be realized physically? We examine the difficulties that we shall encounter as the consequences of our choice. The difficulties are themselves problems of design at one level lower in the structural hierarchy. We gather evidence that reflects the apparent ability to resolve these problems. If among these sub-problems are some whose resolution is too uncertain, then possible solutions for them must be conceived and considered, and the consequent difficulties, which now constitute design problems at a level still lower, must be examined to see whether they can be resolved. It is somewhat analogous to playing chess, wherein the consequences of the present move are examined by considering the consequence of a second move and possibly that of a third move before a final decision is made.

We have asserted that intensity of belief is one of the important factors to be considered in the question of physical realizability. What is the nature of this belief? Essentially, it is a belief that a physically realizable design can be accomplished without exceeding a specified budget of time and money for the work of design. Belief in matters of this kind is seldom absolute; usually some residue of uncertainty remains until the task is almost accomplished. After the task is actually completed all doubt is removed; the object of belief has become a fact. In this context, belief is akin to confidence as used in statistical analysis. Indeed, it is a subjective confidence that we can, in principle, express as a probability that a physically realizable design can be achieved while spending in time and money an amount for design work less than, or at most equal to, the allowed budget. We wish to emphasize the two elements that are involved here. Firstly, there are confidence limits; these correspond to the limits of the permissable spending range, namely from zero up to and including the allowed budget. Inasmuch as the allowed budget can be set explicitly at some arbitrary amount of time and money, it is an objective quantity. Second, we test the strength of our belief and thereby make a judgment about our level of confidence. For example, we might judge our level of confidence to be .95 on a probability scale that ranges from zero to one. This is clearly a subjective estimate.

It may be irksome to some people who deal habitually with objective quantities to accept the idea of making subjective estimates. But in the world of reality we are continually compelled to make such estimates, whether we are willing or not, and to make them explicitly. To make critical decisions in a rational way, in either professional or personal affairs, requires an intensive probing of our state of belief. Will the advantages, which are anticipated from a particular one of the several alternative courses of action open to us, be gained indeed? Or will the advantages be forfeited because we were unable to execute the action in a successful manner? Before we actually choose a particular action, what do we believe is our probability of successfully carrying it out? It is precisely at this point in our chain of reasoning that we make a subjective estimate of our chances. We can elect to leave this estimate implicit and submerged beneath our impressions, or we can try to draw it out in an explicit statement as a quantitative expression of our level of confidence. As in other kinds of activities, practice and experience lead to skill in performing such estimates explicitly.

A THEORY OF PHYSICAL REALIZABILITY

We are now able to posit a theory of physical realizability; actually it is a theory about subjective confidence or belief that a given design concept can be physically realized within the limits of a specified design budget. First, intensity of belief is an increasing function of favorable evidence that sub-problems can be resolved. Second, intensity of belief is an increasing function of the size of the budget that will be allowed for the design of that particular part of the system. Third, as expenditures from the design budget are made, favorable evidence will accumulate; and for reasonable amounts of evidence there will be a linear relationship between favorable evidence and expenditures. Fourth, if the rate of increase of favorable evidence with expenditure is high, the intensity of belief in a realizable outcome will be correspondingly high. Fifth, a sufficiently intense belief that a concept is physically realizable will predispose a rational decision maker to favor that concept.

Symbolically we can write,

$$L = f\left[E,\ X_B \left(\frac{dE}{dX}\right)_0\right]$$

where:

L = confidence level on a probability scale from zero to one.
E = amount of favorable evidence in decibels (see next section for explanation)
X = current expenditure in dollars, $\quad 0 \leqslant X \leqslant X_B$
X_B = allowed budget in dollars

$\left(\dfrac{dE}{dX}\right)_0$ = Initial rate of increase in favorable evidence with expenditure

Prior discussion has indicated that X_B is a composite budget of time and money for the design problem. There will be many such budgets since the particular problem is only one of a whole network of problems constituting the entire design project. If we can establish an equivalence between time and money, then X_B can be expressed as a scalar quantity in common units, for example in dollars. This can usually be done well enough for present purposes; but if not, X_B remains a vector quantity, the same comment applying to X also, and each of the components must be treated separately.

The term $(dE/dX)_0$ indicates the ease with which questions of physical realizability are resolved. We take this as a measure of tractability. Finally, level of confidence (that is, intensity of belief) is a function of the amount of evidence, the size of the design budget, and the tractability. Since the level of confidence can reach at most the value one, that is, complete confidence, we visualize a family of surfaces, each a function of E and X_B and parametrically distinguished by $(dE/dX)_0$, which asymptotically

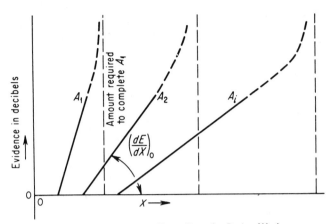

FIG. 9.1 Current Expenditure for Design Work.

approach the level plane of complete confidence as favorable evidence is adduced or a greater budget is allowed. In particular the surface representing design problems with high tractability will make the most rapid approach to the asymptotic plane (see Figure 9.1).

TWO HYPOTHESES ABOUT SELECTION CRITERIA

Hypothesis I: We will assume that a rational decision rule is to select that design concept from among the proffered alternative solutions, that at once has the most favorable list of expected advantages and is judged to be reasonably certain of physical realizability. We must explore the significance of the qualifying word, *reasonable*, as used in the above rule. Which of the three factors that contribute to confidence in physical realizability is the most significant:–the prior evidence that a realization can be achieved, the cost of carrying out the design, or the tractability? We set forth a second hypothesis about the relative importance of these factors:–

Hypothesis II. In the earlier phases of a design (e.g., the Feasibility Study, the Preliminary Design, and the first part of the Detailed Design), tractability, through its effect on the level of confidence, is the more important selection criterion. In the later stages of the Detailed Design when ultimate hardware is being considered, the cost of producing a realizable design, as compared to a reasonable budget in time and money, is the predominant criterion.

We have hypothesized two criteria that we can use as conceptual instruments for gauging our level of confidence that a realizable design can be attained within the budgetary limit. The first one is tractability. It is the important criterion in the early stages of a design project when design concepts are comparatively abstract and the ultimate bits and pieces of hardware are still remote. In the early stages the design is fluid and the conceptual maneuverability is wide because the constraints of other inter-acting parts of the system have not become tight. We ask:–are we going in a useful direction? is it really possible this way? is it reasonably clear that this concept will not lead us later into an insoluble sub-problem? will the choice of this concept unnecessarily restrict our future freedom of action and prevent us from making good decisions later in the design? These questions bear on the tractability of the proposed design concept; this means that when we look carefully one or two steps ahead in the design, no insoluble problems are visible.

Later, when the last layers of sub-problems become visible, and a great many small design problems are being simultaneously attacked, the interest shifts to questions of cost. Many designers and draftsmen are committed to the task, and the total design budget is being depleted rapidly. The fear of going down a blind alley has receded because the end can be seen more clearly. The attention is on the immediate problem, and it is not distracted by concern over subproblems that might be engendered by a proposed solution. The designer seeks, and his supervisor demands, a high level of confidence in the realizability of the chosen solution, since now an ill-chosen solution for a relatively small design problem might place the entire project in jeopardy. Because much of the system has been designed and irrevocably fixed, severe constraints restrict the range of possible solutions. For these reasons the choice is forced to fall on solutions that are practically certain to work. Only such solutions are permissible. The question becomes:–among the solutions, all of which are practically certain to work, which are most likely to fall within an allowed, or rea-sonable, budget of time and money? As the end of the project is approached, the predominating criterion becomes the expected cost of the design work relative to the budget.

THE PROCESS OF RESOLVING PHYSICAL REALIZABILITY

As we study a proposed concept we are likely to get both favorable and unfavorable evidence to support the hypothesis that the concept can be resolved into a physically realizable design. There is some similarity to the classical learning process as exemplified by an animal in a maze. In design work various possibilities are probed; those which lead to unresolvable difficulties give negative evidence. However, other probes allow deeper penetration, and a final resolution of the problem becomes more visible. Although elements of random trial are present, at least two factors dis-tinguish rational behavior from lower forms of goal-oriented or problem-solving behavior. In the first place, if a probe in a particular direction proves unsuccessful, we seek out the reasons. Not only is that direction eliminated, but a whole class of directions, which would be unfavorable for similar reasons, is also eliminated. It is more or less like playing the game of twenty questions in which the shrewd participant begins by eliminating whole categories, then classes and subclasses, until the particular item is isolated. In the second place, favorable evidence is distinguished from unfavorable because it is gauged by the extent to which subproblems are resolvable. In many problem situations the ultimate goal is known to the searcher, but he either does not use, or does not have available, any instruments for discriminating between positive and negative approaches to the goal. Under such conditions it is only by chance that the searcher performs a successful combination of steps leading to the goal.

The skilled designer is not only goal-oriented; *he also understands the process for reaching the goal.* Although he makes trials, he avoids repeating errors; and further, he seeks positive indications of the realizability of his solutions before he goes too far in a given direction. His behavior resembles that of a navigator in an uncharted sea who knows his ultimate destination, but must depend on his instruments as he steers his way around obstacles.

THE NATURE OF EVIDENCE

We have said that evidence changes our state of belief; that the state of belief can be made explicit as a level of confidence; and, in particular, that favorable evidence increases our level of confidence.* We wish to put this idea into a quantitative framework. Recall that the level of confidence, L, is measured on a probability scale. Let A_i represent the proposition that the ith one of the set of alternative design concepts can be physically realized, and $P(A_i)$ the probability that the proposition is true. From our previous discussion we observe that in this form the probability statement can not be translated into a level of confidence because the latter was conditioned by the allowed budget, X_B. To facilitate such a translation we express the conditional relationship as $A_i \mid X_B$ meaning thereby the proposition, A_i, given the budget, X_B. Now we can write $L = P(A_i \mid X_B)$. Suppose we obtain some additional evidence E. How can this be incorporated in the statement about level of confidence? Symbolically, we can include it in the given conditions. Thus $L = P(A_i \mid EX_B)$; the order of the given conditions is immaterial. However, we should like to separate E so that its effect can be estimated.

To accomplish the separation we develop Baye's theorem. Suppose we consider the significance of the statement $P(A_iE \mid X_B)$. The joint statement A_iE is interpreted as A_i is true and E is true, and hence we are indicating the probability that the joint statement is true. The statement can be decomposed in either one of two symmetrical ways,

$$P(A_iE \mid X_B) = P(A_i \mid EX_B) \cdot P(E \mid X_c)$$
$$= P(E \mid A_iX_B) \cdot P(A_i \mid X_B)$$

The literal translation of the symbolic statement indicates the general notion that the probability of the joint proposition is true is the product

---

* The material in this section has been adapted from a series of lectures given by E. T. Jaynes, summer of 1960 at U.C.L.A.

64

of the separate probabilities. Since the two results are equal to each other we may combine them to obtain a form that will permit us to assess the effect of additional evidence.

$$P(A_i \mid EX_B) = P(A_i \mid X_B) \cdot \frac{P(E \mid A_iX_B)}{P(E \mid X_B)}$$

If each symbol were allowed to stand for any appropriate proposition, this would be Baye's theorem. We observe that $P(A_i \mid X_B)$ was our level of confidence before we obtained the evidence, E; that $P(A_i \mid EX_B)$ is the new level as a result of having E; and that the change is represented quantitatively by the fraction in the right-hand member, which will be greater than one if the evidence is favorable and equal to or less than one otherwise.

Actually, the fraction in Baye's equation is difficult to estimate; but we can recast the equation in terms of odds and obtain a form that is easier to handle intuitively. By odds we mean precisely the same thing that is meant in gambling wagers. Let A_i indicate that the proposition is true and $\bar{A}_i$ that it is false. We assume that the proposition conduces to a clear identification of its truth or falsity; that is, that there is no grey area in which a sharp judgment cannot be made. Since the proposition must be true or false, we have $P(A_i) + P(\bar{A}_i) = 1$. We define the odds as the probability of being true over the probability of being false; thus $O(A_i) = P(A_i)/P(\bar{A}_i)$. The same reasoning will apply when we deal with conditional propositions. Thus

$$O(A_i \mid EX_B) = \frac{P(A_i \mid EX_B)}{P(\bar{A}_i \mid EX_B)}$$

We are now able to write the Baye's theorem equivalents for the numerator and denominator of the fraction in the expressions for the odds.

$$O(A_i \mid EX_B) = \frac{P(A_i \mid X_B)}{P(\bar{A}_i \mid X_B)} \cdot \frac{P(E \mid A_iX_B) \cdot P(E \mid X_B)}{P(E \mid \bar{A}_iX_B) \cdot P(E \mid X_B)}$$

$$= O(A_i \mid X_B) \cdot \frac{P(E \mid A_iX_B)}{P(E \mid \bar{A}_iX_B)}$$

The new odds are equal to the old odds multiplied by a fraction that compares the probability that the evidence in question would have been obtained if A_i is physically realizable to the probability that the same evidence would have been obtained if A_i were not physically realizable, all within the budgetary limit. Indeed, this ratio is a kind of index that relates to the criticalness of the investigation or experiment yielding the evidence.

Since the expression for odds involves a product it is useful to use a logarithmic form. We define the evidence function

$$\mathrm{Ev}_A(A \mid X) \equiv 10 \log_{10} O(A \mid X).$$

Rewriting the equation for odds,

$$\mathrm{Ev}_{A_i}(A_i \mid EX_B) = \mathrm{Ev}_{A_i}(A_i \mid X_B) + 10 \log_{10} \frac{P(E \mid A_iX_B)}{P(E \mid \bar{A}_iX_B)}$$

We can now speak of evidence as measured in decibels. The second term in the right-hand member of the equation is the augment in evidence due to E; it is also measured in decibels. Note that the subscript in the symbol Ev_{A_i} indicates that it is A_i that is negated in the equivalent expression for odds. If the same rule is applied to the augment, even though A_i now appears among the conditions, the revised equation is obtained.

$$\mathrm{Ev}_{A_i}(A_i \mid EX_B) = \mathrm{Ev}_{A_i}(A_i \mid X_B) + \mathrm{Ev}_{A_i}(E \mid A_iX_B)$$

If we had obtained several items of evidence, say $E_1 \ldots E_n$, the equation would be extended to

$$\mathrm{Ev}_{A_i}(A_i \mid E_1 \ldots E_nX_B) = \mathrm{Ev}_{A_i}(A_i \mid X_B) + \sum_{j=1}^{n} \mathrm{Ev}_{A_i}(E_j \mid A_iX_B)$$

If, in the light of some evidence E, the probability that a proposition A is true is one-half, then the odds are one, and the evidence to support the truth of A is precisely zero. It requires an infinite amount of favorable evidence to bring the probability to one; and, conversely, an infinite amount of unfavorable evidence to reduce the probability to zero. The tabular values of Table 9.1 indicate the relation between evidence and level of confidence.

TABLE 9.1

RELATION BETWEEN EVIDENCE AND LEVEL OF CONFIDENCE

Favorable		Unfavorable	
Evidence Decibels	Level of Confidence Percent	Evidence Decibels	Level of Confidence
∞	100	−∞	0
20	99	−20	1
13	95	−13	5
9.5	90	−9.5	10
3	66	3	33
0	50	0	50

ESTIMATION OF EVIDENCE

Suppose that we are investigating the physical realizability of one particular design concept. Among the several subproblems that appear, one pertains to resisting oxidation at some elevated temperature. In attempting to resolve this subproblem, we conceive several plausible concepts, one being a metal, hotly sprayed with ceramic. We plan to simulate the field conditions in the laboratory with a suitable sample, but we cannot be sure that we shall be able to duplicate all of the essential conditions of actual operation.

Before we order the experiment we consider how much evidence we might gain from its performance. We reason that if we perform the experiment, there will be an outcome; suppose the outcome is successful in so far as the laboratory is concerned. This will be the evidence, E_j. What significance does E_j have for the ultimate prototype? Suppose, in respect to oxidation, the prototype turns out to be successful, that is, physically realizable; this is the proposition A_i. Now we estimate $P(E_j \mid A_i X_B)$ by asking what the probability is that a part which was able to withstand operating conditions could also pass the laboratory test. It may be that we believe that the laboratory test will be even more severe than the field condition, and therefore we assign a probability of .9 to this quantity.

Now we turn the question around and assume that the prototype has failed, that is, we consider the proposition $\bar{A}_i$. Under these conditions, what is the probability that the sample would have passed the laboratory test, and thereby have furnished the same evidence, E_j, as before? What value will we be willing to assign to $P(E_j \mid \bar{A}_i X_B)$? If we were to say that there was a good chance of the sample testing satisfactorily, say as high as .9, then the augment in evidence would be

$$\mathrm{Ev}_{A_i}(E_j \mid A_i X_B) = 10 \log_{10} (.9/.9)$$
$$= 0$$

Such an experiment would result in no additional evidence. To put it in another way, the test would not be able to discriminate at all between success and failure and therefore could not add to our knowledge. It is worth while commenting that many ill-conceived experiments are performed which yield only a modicum of evidence and which, perhaps, could be avoided with this kind of preliminary, but quantitative, soul-searching.

On the other hand, if the estimate of the latter probability had been .1, then

$$\mathrm{Ev}_{A_i}(E_j \mid A_i X_B) = 10 \log_{10} (.9/.1) = 9.5 \text{ db.}$$

If the original level of confidence, $P(A_i \mid X_B)$, of being able to resolve the question of physical realizability for this concept within the budgetary limit, had been .8, then

$$\mathrm{Ev}_{A_i}(A_i \mid X_B) = 10 \log_{10} (.8/.2) = 6 \text{ db}$$

Hence the newly established evidence would be

$$\mathrm{Ev}_{A_i}(A_i \mid E_j X_B) = 6 + 9.5 = 15.5 \text{ db}$$

This amount of evidence would correspond to odds of 35.5 or a level of confidence of about .97, probably good enough to gamble, except where the penalty for failure is very severe. Under the circumstances we should feel inclined to set up the tests, although we should wish to estimate the cost in order to be assured that the evidence would not be too costly.

ESTIMATIONS OF TRACTABILITY

In judging the tractability of a proposed concept, we examine the tractability of the subproblems to which it gives rise. If any of the subproblems suggests solutions that quickly appear to be physically realizable (high rate of evidence-generation for low expenditure) we consider them very tractable. Our interest focuses on those about which there is uncertainty. Let A_{ijk} . . . refer to the kth proposed solution to the jth design problem, Q_{ij} . . ., which in turn stems from a proposed solution, A_i . . ., one level higher in the project.* The structural relation between problems and proposed solutions, and the meaning of the subscripts, are shown in Figure 9.2.

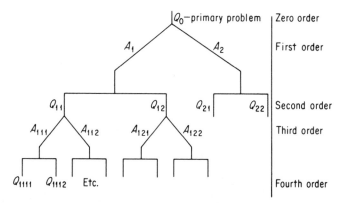

FIG. 9.2 The Tree Structure of a Design Project. (Adapted from Marples, *The Decisions of Engineering Design.*)

We begin with a primary problem, Q_o, which is, indeed, the original engineering statement of the problem, resulting from the initial activity analysis. A number of plausible solutions are proposed; these are $A_1, A_2 \ldots A_n$. We will only consider the first two in each of the steps, although the extension to any number will follow from the same reasoning. Each of the proposed solutions, when investigated for physical realizability, will give rise to a number of subproblems. Thus A_1 will create Q_{11} and Q_{12}; while A_2 will create Q_{21} and Q_{22}. If these problems are not clearly resolvable, then solutions of them are investigated; and the physical realizability of the latter are considered. Thus, proposed solutions of Q_{21} would be A_{211} and

---

* The use of a tree to represent the hierarchial structure of a design project, the corresponding system of nomenclature, and the concepts of tractability and critical decision are adapted from D. L. Marples, *The Decisions of Engineering Design* (London: The Institute of Engineering Designers, July 1960).

A_{212}. The process continues, penetrating deeper into the hierarchial structure, until a sufficient level of confidence is achieved to enable a critical decision.

We wish to explore how the quality of solutions of subproblems, and their richness in number, provides evidence that reflects on level of confidence. Whether A_1 can be physically realized depends on whether the subproblems Q_{11} and Q_{12} can be jointly resolved. In propositional terms this is equivalent to $A_1 = Q_{11} \cdot Q_{12}$; and the probabilities associated with them are accordingly $P(A_1) = P(Q_{11} \cdot Q_{12})$. If we assume that the two subproblems are substantially independent of each other (for example, one problem may have to do with the shape of a part, and the other with finding an appropriate corrosion-resisting material) then the equation can be decomposed into $P(A_1) = P(Q_{11}) \cdot P(Q_{12})$. But suppose that one problem does depend on how the other is resolved. For example, if one problem has to do with finding a suitable material to withstand corrosion and the other has to do with providing sharp interior corners in the shape of the part, then fatigue of the material under conditions of corrosion may enter as a secondary factor and restrict the opportunity of finding a proper material. When there is a dependence, it is indicated as $P(Q_{12} \mid Q_{11})$ and $P(A_1) = P(Q_{11}) \cdot P(Q_{12} \mid Q_{11})$.

In either of the foregoing cases both problems must have physically realizable solutions if A_1 is to be realizable. Therefore, we examine the possible solutions to each problem. The problem Q_{11} can be solved if solutions A_{111} or A_{112} are realizable. Accordingly

$$P(Q_{11}) = P(A_{111} + A_{112})$$
$$= P(A_{111}) + P(A_{112}) - P(A_{111} \cdot A_{112}).$$

The term $P(A_{111} \cdot A_{112})$ is subject to the same argument as applied above to $P(Q_{11} \cdot Q_{12})$. If the two solutions are independent, that is, are not variations of a single concept–then $P(A_{111} \cdot A_{112}) = P(A_{111}) \cdot P(A_{112})$. Otherwise the conditional probabilities are used.

To illustrate, suppose that upon investigating A_{111} and A_{112} in a preliminary way we estimate a level of confidence of 0.9 for each relative to their realizability within a reasonable budget, and that the two concepts are independent; then $P(Q_{11}) = 0.9 + 0.9 - (0.9 \times 0.9) = 0.99$. If we are satisfied with a confidence level of 0.95, then at this point we are in a satisfactory state.

A word of caution, however, must be given in order to avoid unwarranted overconfidence. Usually the proposed solutions are not completely independent. Two apparently different solutions may make the same difficult demands on material or on fabrication methods or on reliability of critical components. In general, when multiple solutions are available, there may be a tendency to overstate the derived level of confidence. If in the example above $P(A_{111} \cdot A_{112}) = P(A_{111}) \cdot P(A_{112} \mid A_{111})$, and

$P(A_{112} \mid A_{111}) = 1$, that is, A_{112} is certain if A_{111} is, then

$$P(Q_{11}) = 0.9 + 0.9 - 0.9 \times 1.0$$
$$= 0.9.$$

In other words, if both solutions depend on the same critical factors, then having two solutions does not add to our confidence. If the dependence is only partial, then a corresponding improvement will result.

The same argument, indicating the possibility of overconfidence when a problem is examined in the light of several proposed alternative solutions, leads to the conclusion that we may be too disparaging when estimating the probability of resolving a particular solution in terms of its constituent problems. The question of dependence among interrelated probabalistic events must be considered carefully. We return to the original example. Suppose a similar calculation for Q_{12} indicates 0.97. If the problems are independent, we can calculate $P(A_1) = 0.99 \times 0.97 = 0.96$, which is just over the 0.95 level. However, if our final estimate was 0.85 we should require more evidence before we could come to a critical decision, unless other solutions, for example A_2, were satisfactory. If more evidence is required, we examine the subproblems to see if additional alternative solutions are available, and also probe deeper into the solutions by further analysis and experimental work. We convert the preliminary estimate of confidence level (for example, in the above illustration $P(A_1) = 0.96$) to an evidence function, thus expressing it in decibels. New evidence is obtained, if required, and added to the original until a satisfactory level of confidence is achieved, or until a rejection is indicated, because further effort toward a physically realizable design based on that concept appears uneconomical in relation to a reasonable budget.

A SELECTION RULE

We return to the question of final selection among the surviving proposed design concepts. Each has its array of advantages; each is believed to be realizable within a reasonable design budget with more or less confidence. We will, in this discussion, assume that we are able to set up a weighting function over the set of advantages, which are material to the decision. We thereby make the advantages commensurable on an appropriate utility scale. This permits plotting a point for each concept on coordinate scales of utility and confidence (figure 9.3). The outer points such as A, B, and C form a convex set. These dominate the inner points, therefore they alone need be con-

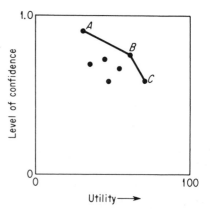

FIG. 9.3 The Set of Dominant Design Concepts.

sidered. If it turns out that one particular concept dominates all of the others (that is, has the highest rating for advantages, and also the highest level of confidence), then this would be the natural one to select. However, if several concepts appear in the convex set, we need a rule for selecting from among them.

There is no unique rule for discriminating among the alternative concepts in the convex set. One reasonable rule is to choose that one which presents the highest expectation of gain. For the ith concept in the convex set, let L_i be the confidence level and V_i be the value assigned to the advantages. We will assume that if the concept were selected and it were to fail of realization, the loss would be S_i. The expected gain is

$$E(G_i) = L_i V_i - (1 - L_i) S_i$$

We seek out in this way that concept for which $E(G)$ is a maximum. The loss resulting from a failure will usually be the same for all of the concepts, except for those which require extraordinary commitments. An example will illustrate the rule. Suppose there are three concepts in the convex set, A_1 with $L_1 = 0.98$, $V_1 = 100$; A_2 with $L_2 = 0.95$, $V_2 = 200$; A_3 with $L_3 = 0.90$, $V_3 = 300$. The loss is assumed to be 1000 for all three. Then

$$E(G_1) = 0.98 \times 100 - 0.02 \times 1000 = 78,$$

$$E(G_2) = 0.95 \times 200 - 0.05 \times 1000 = 140,$$

and

$$E(G_3) = 0.90 \times 300 - 0.10 \times 1000 = 170$$

Accordingly the third alternative would be chosen. Had the loss been assumed to be greater, say 4000 for all three, then $E(G_1) = 18$, $E(G_2) = -10$, and $E(G_3) = -130$. In this case the first alternative is preferred to either of the others, and the second is preferred to the third. We note that when the penalty for failure is small, the level of confidence can be lower; but when the penalty is very high the level of confidence must be correspondingly high in order to insure against catastrophic losses.

A THEORY OF CRITICAL DECISION MAKING IN DESIGN

The various parts of a theory of making critical decisions in engineering design are to hand. We wish to assemble them into a single statement.

(1) A critical decision is formal, and is assumed to be final. When one of the proffered set of possible. solutions of the design problem under consideration is formally chosen, important commitments are made by the management of the project. Design effort is released to proceed from the preliminary explorations of the particular concept to a final state of physical realization. Such paralleling subprojects in other parts of the design as need to be coordinated proceed on the assurance that the particular concept shall be realized. Only under the most compelling circumstances is the selected concept retracted and a substitute introduced,

for the penalty of such a virtual failure is usually very high in terms of its effect on both the direct and the indirect design work committed by the decision for that concept.

(2) A critical decision rests principally on a comparison of advantages and difficulties associated with each of the proffered solutions. The advantages may be evaluated in principle on some utility scale. The difficulties generally emerge as subproblems that must be resolved if that particular concept of solution is to be capable of physical realization.

(3) Design work is constrained by a budget of time and money. Actual budgets are usually set for the major phases of the design project. In some projects where tight control is maintained, time and money budgets are set for each of the major problems as it is recognized. In others only time-targets are set for such problems so that the project as whole can be coordinated. Even when budgets are not set, it is assumed that the design work will be done within the limits of a reasonable budget .

(4) A critical decision depends on the levels of confidence held for each of the contending solutions. We assume that any physically possible concept could, with probability *one*, be developed into a physically realizable design if an indefinitely large budget of time and money is allowed. However, the budget is always limited either by edict or by a sense of the reasonable. The level of confidence, as used here, is a subjective probability that the design work required to bring the particular concept to a state of physical realizability will fall within the limits of a decreed or assumed budget.

(5) The level of confidence is affected by evidence. Initially, we develop a level of confidence in each of the alternatives by an internal reaction, tempered by experience and the similar reactions of others. We try to anticipate the range of subproblems that will appear when the concept is pressed toward a realizable design, and we consider the inherent difficulties in their solution. All of these preliminary activities combine to form an initial level of confidence. Some of the alternatives may be dropped after this cursory study. The principal contenders may require further evidence, which is obtained by analysis, by experiment, by consultation, by searching relevant literature, or by exploring personal and group experience. This evidence, reflecting on a particular concept, augments the initial level of confidence.

(6) Critical decisions emphasize levels of confidence early in the design project, shifting to costs of design work as the project progresses. In the early stages of a design, the concepts are more abstract and therefore further from physical realization. Close cost estimates of design work are difficult to make. When advantages are more or less equal, critical decisions hinge on relative levels of confidence for the competing concepts. The chosen one will reflect emphasis on the level of confidence on which it can be realized. In the late stages where physical realization is easier to assess, only concepts with a high level of confidence are acceptable; and, when advantages are similar, critical decisions rest on the relative design costs

(that is, on the confidence limits of the budget). If advantages are equivalent, that concept which requires the least design effort will be favored.

(7) Critical decisions take account of the severity of the penalty resulting from the failure of a chosen concept to attain to a state of physical realizability. If the penalty in redoing committed design work, or in failing to meet a time target, is very severe, the selection rule will require a high level of confidence. If the penalty is mild, the level of confidence can be relaxed correspondingly.

(8) A critical design decision should be made by a person at that level of administration at which he could be properly required to bear the responsibility if the chosen concept failed.

chapter

10

ARCHETYPES

AND COMPUTERS

It is a matter of practical expediency to construct an archetype in the abstract before constructing a prototype in the material. The elements from which the archetypes are constructed are largely the idealizations of physical phenomena that constitute the engineering sciences. These idealizations are also represented mathematically, but each is descriptive of a class of phenomena rather than being specific to a particular design situation. In order to achieve the useful quality of generalization, the phenomena must be isolated from the complicating environment so that the "pure" phenomena are not contaminated by other factors. The object of a design, however, is usually embedded in its environment and involves several of the idealized phenomena, interacting with one other. Furthermore, it is frequently enmeshed with economic factors and other considerations. More often than not, the archetype of a design concept must be custom made for each individual case, using the mathematical idealizations of the engineering sciences as the building blocks.

The building of an archetype is so contingent upon the particular design situation and the specific design concept that the construction of a detailed procedure for accomplishing this does not seem practical. However, some general principles can be set down.* Our problem situation here is to construct a mathematical archetype; hence we can deal with this as with any other problem using the method of approach outlined in Chapter 7 under the design process.

Firstly, we have to analyze the problem situation. We define our goal; we ask: Which aspects of the behavior or performance of the design object are relevant to the superior goals one echelon higher in the design? Which basic phenomena are involved? What are the constraining factors that will influence the design object when it is incorporated in that part of the system to which it belongs? We then ask: How do the several relevant phenomena involved in the design concept relate to each other? What are the appropriate design parameters, and what are the input, output variables? Which design constants are needed? Which factors are important enough to be used in setting up the criterion function for measuring the performance of the design object? At the first attempt, perhaps only partial answers to these questions will be achieved; we may have to return to them later as our understanding of the problem increases. At any rate we will essay the first formulation of the problem statement. It will include a restatement of the design concept and the principles on which it is presumed to operate; it will state the aspects of performance that are considered to be important and that should possibly be included in a criterion of performance; it will indicate the constraints that are to be imposed on the design and the physical phenomena that account for its behavior.

Second, we attempt to synthesize a general description of the design concept in terms of the parameters and variables that are relevant to the situation. We propose the appropriate idealizations, drawn mainly from the engineering sciences, which appear to fit the phenomena involved in the functions of the proposed object. We determine the nature of the interrelations between the several phenomena and note the parameters that are common to them.

Third, we write the specific equations to fit the design concept and the performance aspects of interest. Each individual phenomenon is likely to involve a separate equation to describe its function in the overall behavior of the design object. Also, we assemble into a criterion function the factors that constitute the important considerations in measuring the suitability and value of the specific design. We bear in mind that the mathematical archetype, which we are now assembling, will represent a particular family

* See D. W. Ver Planck and B. R. Teare, Jr., *Engineering Analysis* (New York: John Wiley & Sons, Inc., 1954) for many examples of constructing mathematical archetypes in design situations. See also their formulation of the professional method for dealing with such problems on pages 28 and 29.

of designs, and the criterion must be able to distinguish between the more and the less desirable of them.

Fourth, we confront the mathematical archetype with whatever real experience or known results are available to test its validity. Possibly we may be able to check it by some other parallel approach. We push it to one limit or another to see whether the results are reasonable. If difficulties arise, as often happens, revisions of the formulation may be necessary.

Fifth, we look for simplifications of the formulation. We summarize the mathematical description verbally and graphically; this helps us to form a mental picture of the complex of phenomena which will be useful in the next steps of design, and which will enable us to prepare a simplified communication of the ideas to others.

In the next sections we shall illustrate these general procedures by preparing the archetypes that will be used in Chapter 12, "Techniques of Optimization." Reread the general procedure as you follow through the illustrations.

AN ARCHETYPE FOR A SUBSYSTEM

Electrical energy is to be generated in a hydroelectric plant at a remote dam site and is to be transmitted 200 miles to a step-down transformer station for distribution at 11 kilovolts. The power transmission line is one of the principal subsystems in the proposed overall power system. We wish to set up an archetype that will reflect the economic behavior of the transmission line.

The proposed system will be coupled with an existing system of local steam plants. The plan is to draw a steady load from the hydroelectric plant equal to its rated capacity, and to allow the load on the steam plants to fluctuate with the variations in total demand. The design concept of the transmission line is the conventional one of an overhead 3 conductor system supported from insulator strings suspended on transmission line towers. The necessary synchronous condensers are contemplated to improve the voltage regulation and to correct the power factor.

We will follow the general approach outlined in the preceding section.

(1) *The Problem Situation:*–The general objective of the system design is to exploit the natural advantages of the site at the most economically favorable level considering the long term needs of the community. A subobject, relevant to the design of the power transmission subsystem, is to achieve the lowest annual cost for transmitting the amount of energy which the system analysis indicates to be optimum for the situation.

Some of the phenomena involved in the functioning of the transmission line are:–energy losses owing to electrical resistance; energy losses and electrical breakdown because of corona effects at high voltages; effects of distributed capacitance and inductance on voltage regulation and power factor; transient surges of energy due to switching operations and lightning discharges; stresses on towers, insulators, and conductors caused by the weight of conductors and hardware and by wind and sleet loads.

Some of the constraints imposed on the transmission line are:–the constant electrical load which it must transmit, the requirement of protection against flash-over caused by transient voltages, the tensile strength of the conductors and other stressed hardware, and the availability of tower sites which depends on the route and the terrain. Energy losses by electrical resistance and by corona will be related. Lower resistance loss is favored by higher voltage; lower corona loss by lower voltage. Voltage regulation phenomena will be related to corona losses because the latter are reduced by increasing the outside diameter of the conductors and by increasing the spacing between them; but these changes increase the reactance of the line. In order to reduce the size of the illustration we will consider here only the phenomena concerned with resistance losses and corona effects.

The design parameters relevant to the economic performance of the line in respect to resistance losses and corona effects are:

E = transmission line voltage between conductors at the power plant in KV

I = line current in amp

C = line conductance per conductor in mho

S = spacing between conductors in ft

D = outside diameter of the conductor in in. The input variable is the line current at the power plant in amperes. The output variables are:

E_1 = line voltage at the distribution end in kv

I_1 = line current at the distribution end in amp

To simplify the presentation, we will take $E_1 = E$ and $I_1 = I$.

Other information items that will appear as constants or fixed coefficients in the formulation are:

K_1 = constant power generated at the hydroelectric plant, $5 \times 10^4 \, KW$

k_1 = value of delivered power (based on $0.01 kwhr), 87.5 $/kwyr

k_2 = cost per mho of conductance per conductor for the length of the transmission line (based on cost of copper conductor at $0.35 per lb), 13×10^6 $/mho

k_3 = incremental cost per kilovolt of transmission line voltage, 10^4 $/kv

i = rate of imputed charges ascribed to invested capital, 0.10 $/$yr

The important factors which should appear in a criterion function relate to the cost of operating the transmission line. Included should be the value of the power losses, the cost imputed to the conductors which will depend on their size, and the costs imputed to the system voltage which depend on the size of towers, spacing of conductors, size of insulators and other high tension hardware all of which become larger and more costly as the line voltage is increased.

(2) *Synthesis:*–Power is dissipated by the resistance of the line. The loss per conductor is I^2R, or I^2C^{-1} in terms of conductance. The total loss, neglecting the variation in current along the line, is $3.10^{-3}I^2C^{-1}$. Power is also dissipated by corona discharge. However, if the line voltage is set below a critical value, which depends on the outside diameter of the conductor and the spacing, the corona loss is very small. Operating below the critical voltage has the advantage of reducing the danger of flashover from dirt or inclement weather. This requires that we set up a constraint on the line voltage so that its normal value will be some fraction of the critical voltage, say 0.95. The critical voltage is $E_c = k_4D \ln 24S/D$ where the coefficient, k_4 is related to the disruptive gradient and is a function of barometric pressure, ambient temperature, and the surface roughness of the conductors. Under standard conditions, with a stranded and weathered conductor $k_4 = 22.8$ kv/in. to ground.

The critical voltage, E_c, and hence the operating voltage, can be increased by making either D or S larger. However, D affects the result much more rapidly than S, that is, E_c is not sensitive to S; hence S can be accommodated to the requirements of the tower design. We will assume that $S = 10$ ft is a reasonable value. At an increase in cost the design parameter D can be made larger for a given conductance C by using a hollow conductor. However, to avoid complicating this presentation we will consider only the solid conductor. The conductance and the diameter are physically related; $D = k_5C^{1/2}$. For copper, considering the total length of the line, $k_5 = 3.38$ in./mho$^{1/2}$.

We observe that a choice of D simultaneously influences the resistance loss and the critical voltage. Thus, increasing D reduces the resistance loss and increases the permissable operating voltage; both effects reduce the annual cost of dissipated energy. At the same time, the investment is increased, and the imputed annual cost accordingly increases.

(3) *Execution.*–The power to be transmitted is

$$K_1 = \sqrt{3}\ EI$$

If we replace D by its equivalent value in C, the permissable maximum operating voltage between conductors is

$$E_m = 0.95\sqrt{3}\ k_4k_5C^{1/2} \ln \frac{24S}{C^{1/2}k_5}$$

This relation defines a constraint on the design parameter E, thus with a rearrangement of terms

$$E \leq 1.65\ k_4k_5C^{1/2}(\ln 24S - \tfrac{1}{2} \ln C - \ln kS)$$

Since, by applying the constraint on the operating voltage, the corona loss has been virtually eliminated, we consider only the worth of the resistance loss. This is $3.10^{-3}\ k_1I^2C^{-1}$ dollars/yr. The investment in conductors is $3k_2C$ dollars, and the incremental investment in equipment to accommodate

77

the selected voltage is k_3E dollars. The portion of the total operating cost which is relevant to the archtype here developed is

$$U = 3 \cdot 10^{-3}k_1I^2C^{-1} + i(3k_2C + k_3E)$$

This is the cost we wish to minimize; it is, therefore, the criterion by which to judge any particular design. At this particular stage, we mean by a design the assignment of specific values to the design parameters E and C.

(4) *Checking and Revision:*–We may introduce the numerical values of the coefficients and constants in order to test the reasonableness of the results. The criterion function and the behavioral relations become:

$$U = 0.263I^2C^{-1} + 3.9 \cdot 10^6C + 10^3E$$

$$\psi_1 = 1.73EI - 5 \cdot 10^4 = 0$$

$$\phi_1 = 63.5C^{1/2}(8.52 - \ln C) - E \geq 0$$

Within the limits of the assumptions and omissions, and for the express purposes for which this archetype was constructed, this set of relations represents the physical and economic performance of the power transmission line. Suppose we assume that $E = 150$ kv; then $I = 193$ amp. From ϕ_1, C must be equal at least to 0.040 mho per conductor, and $D = .676$ in. The criterion function obtains the value $U = 5.50 \cdot 10^5$ dollars per yr. There is

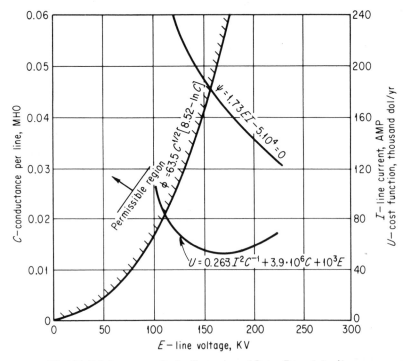

FIG. 10.1 Relations among Design Parameters of Power Transmission Line.

no reason to believe that it is near the optimum; therefore some other combination of permissable parameter values may be better. In the next chapter we will consider the analytical techniques of optimization.

5. *Implementation and Presentation*:–Figure 10.1 displays graphically the required relation, ψ_1, between current and voltage to meet the power demand. The relation between the critical voltage and the size of the conductor, as measured by its total conductance C, is shown by ϕ_1. The selected voltage must be in the permissable region. If we use the minimum values of C for each voltage we can calculate corresponding values for U, the cost function. The resulting graph of U indicates a minimum value at $E = 165$ kv. We cannot tell yet whether this is a true minimum, as a higher value for C may reduce the resistance loss enough to compensate for the additional investment in conductors. Even after resolving this question we may still be able to improve the cost by some additional increase in voltage which would now be permissable with the larger conductors. Actually, the value obtained is close to the minimum. When a few parameters are involved, such calculations can be made by trial and error; however, in large problems with many parameters this is not likely to be possible. Finally, we observe that the criterion function is rather flat in the vicinity of the minimum U. This is often, although not always, the case. In this design we could raise the voltage to 180 kv with only a slight effect on U. If some other aspect of the design would be favored by such a change, we could make the accommodation with little penalty. A knowledge of the sensitivity of the design to the several parameters permits the designer to use judgement in making such adjustments.

AN ARCHETYPE FOR A PART

A flywheel-like mass, weighing 2000 lb., is required to rotate in a fixed position at a velocity of approximately 100 radians/sec. The design concept proposes a journal and two oil lubricated sleeve bearings (see Fig. 11.3). Provision has already been made for a central forced-lubrication system to which the proposed bearings could be connected. The bearings, one on each side of the rotating mass, will each take half of the load. Bending of the shaft is neglected, because the span between bearings is to be short. The oil supply pressure, which is to be maintained in the system as a whole, is high enough to ensure a large flow of oil through the bearings with very little rise in temperature. The oil for the system has already been selected At the predicted operating temperature the viscosity is $\mu = 10^{-6}$ lb sec/sq in.

A substantial number of machines are to be produced. One of the objectives of the overall design is to maximize performance, consistent wth a prescribed level of reliability. At the present stage we wish to design the bearings and the journal to accord with this objective.

When a journal, carrying a substantial load, is at rest in a bearing, it squeezes out the oil between itself and the bearing-surface until a very thin surface film remains which, at the high points of the surfaces, is essentially maintained by molecular attraction between the metal and the oil. The journal is eccentric in the bearing with almost no clearance on the underneath side and practically full clearance on the upper side. When it is set in rotation, the journal must shear the oil which surrounds it. In doing so it drags oil into the constricted space beneath it, acting somewhat like a pump. The oil, which the journal drags down and around, forces it to rise and thus to decrease the eccentricity. A steady state film, caused by this dynamic action, is established which acts as a lubricating cushion between the sliding surfaces. Clearly, the equilibrium configuration will occur when the hydraulic pressure on the underside of the journal just balances the load on it. If the load is increased, the thickness of the film at the minimum point, where near tangency occurs, is decreased, and the pressure is increased until the load is again balanced. With too large a load, the film is reduced until high points on the journal come into metallic contact with high points on the bearing. Almost instantaneously, very high temperatures are induced at the points of metal-to-metal rubbing, causing local welding and seizing of the bearing. However, before this catastrophic failure occurs, the film is reduced to such an extent that fine dust and other gritty particles suspended in the oil will induce accelerated wear.

We shall have to consider the following phenomena. The journal, rotating in an oil-filled space induces by viscous shear a tangential and axial flow of oil. Around the underside, hydraulic pressure is established which supports the load. A stable geometrical configuration results from the balancing of the hydrodynamic forces and the externally-imposed forces on the journal. The configuration has a profound effect on the life of the bearing, and the design must be such as to ensure an appropriate minimum film thickness. Other phenomena occur also. The shaft, in shearing the oil, must do frictional work which heats the oil in the film and change its hydrodynamic properties. The major effect is on the viscosity which changes drastically with temperature. With unforced or restricted flow this effect is of major importance. In this design we shall neglect temperature rise as the design conditions prescribe a high flow rate of oil from an external pump. We shall consider the oil to be admitted via a center oil groove around the bearing into which is tapped the oil pressure line.

The design parameters will comprise the radius of the journal R, the half length of the bearing L (from the center oil groove to the end of the bearing), and the clearance C. The minimum oil film thickness, h_0, is to be regarded as an output variable. Its value depends on the values given to the inputs which are the following:–W, the load per bearing, ω, the rotational speed, and μ, the effective viscosity of the oil. It also depends on the values assigned to the design parameters, R, L, and C.

It is convenient to use an eccentricity ratio ϵ such that $h_0 = C(1 - \epsilon)$. The hydrodynamic analysis* considers the force system on an elementary

---

* For a good account of this analysis see R. R. Slaymaker, *Mechanical Design and Analysis* (New York: John Wiley & Sons, Inc., 1959) pp. 280–95.

80

particle, and by relating the velocity gradients to shearing forces, establishes a relation between flow and pressure. Through the use of the continuity relation, the relative flows in the axial and tangential directions are determined. With this, the pressure distribution, circumferentially and axially, is found; and by integrating over the load-bearing surface of the journal, the total supporting force is calculated as a function of the eccentricity ratio ϵ. The result, called the *load capacity number*, is

$$\frac{P}{\mu\omega} \frac{2C^2}{L} = \frac{\epsilon}{2(1 - \epsilon^2)^2} \left[\pi^2(1 - \epsilon^2) + 16\epsilon^2)^{1/2}\right.$$

The quantity P is the average supporting pressure on the journal; it is equal to $W/4RL$. Hence

$$\frac{2W}{\mu\omega} \cdot \frac{C^2}{RL^3} = P'(\epsilon)$$

where

$$P'(\epsilon) = \frac{\epsilon}{(1 - \epsilon^2)^2} \left[\pi^2(1 - \epsilon^2) + 16\epsilon^2\right]^{1/2}$$

is one half the load capacity number.

In a like manner, by integrating the product of shearing stresses and differential area over the active area of the journal, we can obtain the friction torque, which is

$$M = \mu\omega \frac{R^3 L}{C} \times \frac{4\pi}{\sqrt{1 - \epsilon^2}} \text{ lb in.}$$

The energy dissipated in friction heats the oil; the resulting temperature rise reduces the viscosity of the oil and correspondingly reduces the load-carrying capacity of the bearing. The heat, which is mostly carried away by the oil, is produced at a rate equal to the product of the friction torque and the rotational velocity. It is

$$H = \mu\omega^2 \frac{R^3 L}{C} \times \frac{4\pi}{\sqrt{1 - \epsilon^2}} \text{ in. lb/sec.}$$

These equations, for load, friction, and heat rate, constitute a mathematical archetype for the bearing. By manipulating these, the performance of any specific bearing design can be predicted and related to the design requirements for the whole component. In particular, if we combine this archetype with a criterion function, we have a basis for determining a preferred design. This we shall do in the next chapter.

THE USE OF COMPUTERS IN ENGINEERING DESIGN

Of the resources available to man, time is among the most valuable. It is in conserving this resource that a computer can be of great use to the engineering designer. Formulating a mathematical archetype may take some hours or days to accomplish after the design concept has been envisioned, and exploring the implications of the archetype may take many days and even months of tedious computing if done by hand. A large, high speed computer can often do the equivalent work in minutes. In the past it has generally been uneconomic to explore an archetype, owing to the large cost in time and effort, except for the most critical design problems; consequently, there was little motivation for the designer to build such archetypes, or to develop the necessary analytical skills. It was usually cheaper to build a preliminary prototype and explore its characteristics experimentally. Now that many designers have computers at their disposal, it has become more economical in time, effort, and cost to carry analytical techniques much further. Moreover, it is feasible to explore several alternative ideas with little extra cost.

Computers can be exploited in many more ways to support design activity. Many types of parts are used over and over again in the course of certain design activities. A general archetype can be formulated for a given type of part which frequently recurs, and programmed as a special routine for a computer. The program could make provision for accepting any reasonable set of input variables or output requirements and any suitable criterion function. The output would be the optimal set of design parameters and the performance characteristics of the part. It could include a sensitivity and stability analysis. Such automated design is possible for the common machine elements, structural members, fasteners, basic electrical and hydraulic elements, and so on. Indeed, the bearing, which served as the example in the preceding section, could be so programmed that a bearing design, optimal for a particular design situation, could be obtained directly.

It is possible to extend the concept of automated design to components and even to complicated devices. This is currently being done by the major electrical equipment manufacturers for large power transformers and other electrical machinery. Whether or not to automate a design is a matter of economics. The investment lies primarily in the cost of preparing a large computer program. For an equipment as complex as a large power transformer, the program may require many thousands of hours to prepare. It must, when confronted with a particular set of requirements, be able to make design decisions by means of rules incorporated in the program, so that it can automatically make the best choices among geometrical configurations, materials, cooling methods and other pertinent considerations. After this selection it must find the optimum values for the design parameters. In essence the program must contain in latent form the whole spectrum of transformer designs that accord with the design concepts of the originators. The cost of such a program may be in the tens of thousands of dollars, and even in the hundreds of thousands.

Not only can such a program compute the pertinent design information, but the computer can output the results in the form of manufacturing instructions so that they can go directly to the shop for construction. It can even write the specifications, warranties, and contract to send to the customer. With some kinds of components it is possible to go even farther. Computer-controlled machine tools are used widely. The designer of a complex curved part specifies the analytic curves for the contours; the computer prepares a punched or magnetic tape from the analytic information which designates precise spatial positions at small intervals for the cutters. Subsequently, the tapes control the positioning of the cutter-carrying members of the machine tool thus producing the prescribed contours, and finally the complete part. Similar tapes can also produce mechanical drawings. It is thus possible to go from concept to optimally designed part in one automated step. Although the initial investment in programming is high, when circumstances are favorable the savings in engineering work can be very large.

Such an approach is not limited to components or devices. Whole sub-systems can be given an archetypal description so that they can be programmed for the computer. By linking the programmed subsystems together, complex systems can be simulated on the computer. For example, the high tension power transmission line which we used as an illustration earlier in this chapter could be given a much fuller description, the hydro-electric plant, the dam and reservoir, the water shed and the pertinent statistics about rain, snow and other weather factors, the steam plants and the consumers' loads could also be described and programmed. The outputs of one subsystem could become the inputs of another; by setting up the interaction factors properly, the several subsystems would ·be linked together and its overall performance studied in relation to changes made at the subsystem level. Simulation, which large computers have made possible, is a particularly valuable tool for the preliminary study of proposed large systems.

As we have seen, design is essentially an information-processing activity. In a design project of substantial size, the amount of information to be processed is very large. Computers can easily process massive quantities of information. But there is another side to information handling–its storage and retrieval can become exceedingly difficult and costly. As a project proceeds, a huge amount of documentation is required to record design decisions and the information and rationale that support them. Often, later work and decisions should take earlier work into account, but the task of uncovering relevant prior work may be so time consuming that it is omitted. If the information, as it is generated, is documented on punched cards in a storage and retrieval system, the computer can very quickly carry out a search for relevant information and put it at the disposal of the designer. In a like manner, catalog and other technical information can be stored for convenient retrieval.

It is clear that computers will play an increasingly large role in engineering design. Their use will make greater demands on higher levels of analytical skills; it will displace designers whose work is at the repetitive level; it will place a greater premium on creative and inventive design, it will make available more complete design information; and it will allow a fuller exploration of mathematical archetypes.

<table>
<tr><td>chapter

11</td><td>TECHNIQUES OF

OPTIMIZATION</td></tr>
</table>

In prior chapters we have characterized the variables in design problems as input and output variables and as design parameters. A central problem of design is the fixing of design parameters at proper values. Once we have set these values, we have, in fact, given the general system a quantitative individuality enabling it to accept prescribed sets of input variables and transform them into corresponding unique sets of output variables. If the design parameters have been chosen satisfactorily, the resulting output variables will be acceptable in kind and value, providing, of course, that the original design concept had the potentiality for satisfactory solutions. It is a logical deduction, if we accept the fact that changes in the design parameters will cause concomitant changes in the output variables, that there will be *one* choice among the gamut of satisfactory choices of design parameters, which will be as good as or better than any other. This choice we shall call the *optimal set of design parameters*.

ROLE OF CRITERIA

What do we mean when we say that an optimal set of design parameters is as good as or better than any other feasible selection? We are reminded that the word *good* implies a *value judgment*, and that such judgments have meaning only in reference to *criteria*. The answer to the opening question presupposes that a design criterion has been formed which is appropriate to the particular design problem and suited to its position in the hierarchy of design objectives. The optimal set of design parameters exists only in relation to the criterion; when the latter is altered, a different set of parameters will be obtained, that is, we will have a different design. Thus we can state that, in general, the choice of the criterion profoundly affects the actual design.

Sometimes a design criterion is set for a subordinate element without taking into account the higher design objectives of the part of the system which contains it. Optimizing in relation to such a criterion is called *suboptimization,* because it does not consider the system as a whole. Under fortuitous circumstances the resulting design may fit reasonably well with the rest of the system, but under an adverse choice the consequences could be unfortunate.

We have used criterion in the singular. It may be that there are several criteria in respect to which we would like to optimize the design. Unfortunately, optimizing is possible only under one criterion. However, some compromises are possible. One way is to set up a composite criterion in which each of the component criteria is given a relative weight, thereby establishing, in effect, a single criterion. The other way is to convert the lesser criteria into constraints by giving them some upper or lower limits of acceptance. This means, in practice, that the optimization will be accomplished while the design is pushed to the acceptance limits of the subcriteria.

THE GENERAL FORM OF THE OPTIMIZATION PROBLEM

In Chapter 10 we observed that a mathematical archetype of a design object involved input variables (independent) and output variables (dependent) associated with each other through some transforming mechanism, analytically expressed. The transforming expression includes design parameters which are assumed to be under our control. If we choose a particular set of physically realizable values for these parameters we will effectively fix a design; and for any set of permissible values of the input variables a unique set of values of the output variables will obtain. Now we refer to the criterion function. Some or all of the input and output variables and design parameters will be involved in this function; accordingly, if they are all known, the criterion value can be calculated, thus providing us with a measure of the goodness of the particular design. In general, we shall not know whether this particular choice of design parameters was especially good. We can find out by comparison with other possible choices. If we carry out the same sequence of operations for another set we will obtain a different value for the criterion, and the better of the two choices will be evident. In principle we could make a complete exploration over all physically realizable design parameters, and by elimination finally determine the best set.

In some rare cases we might have an unlimited choice of design parameters, but in the usual design situation they are constrained in two ways. First, the parameters and other variables are connected together by natural laws or empirical relations; for example, the heat content of an object is related to its thermal properties and to its temperature. Such constraints we call *functional constraints* because they spell out functional relations among the parameters and the variables which must hold if the design is to be physically realizable. Second, limits may be imposed on individual parameters or on groups of parameters, in order to insure their physical realizability or their compatibility with the rest of the system and the environment. As we shall see, such limits mark out permissible regions; for this reason we shall call them *regional constraints*. The functional constraints will be distinguished by equalities, the regional by inequalities.

We have now the three constituent elements of the general optimization problem, which are:–(1) the criterion function which, by the proper choice of design parameters, is to be brought to a maximum or a minimum, depending on which one corresponds to an optimum; (2) the functional constraints which essentially constitute the mathematical description of the archetype of the proposed object; (3) the regional constraints, setting the allowable limits on design parameters or on derived groups of parameters representing more complex attributes of the proposed object.

MATHEMATICAL REPRESENTATION OF THE GENERAL OPTIMIZATION PROBLEM

We will lump all of the variables together so that the set $(x_1 \ldots x_n)$ will be design parameters in part, input variables in part, and output variables in the remainder. The criterion will be represented by U, which takes on the values of the criterion function $U(x_1 \ldots x_n)$. The set of functional constraints will be represented by $(\psi_1 \ldots \psi_m)$ and the regional constraints by $(\phi_1 \ldots \phi_p)$. Of the regional constraints, the ith one will be constrained between the lower limit l_i and the upper limit L_i. The optimization problem is described by the following set of equations.

$$U = U(x_1 \ldots x_n) \rightarrow \text{optimum}$$
$$\psi_1 = \psi_1(x_1 \ldots x_n) = 0$$
$$\cdot$$
$$\cdot$$
$$\cdot$$
$$\psi_m = \psi_m(x_1 \ldots x_n) = 0$$
$$l_1 \leq \phi_1(x_1 \ldots x_n) \leq L_1$$
$$\cdot$$
$$\cdot$$
$$\cdot$$
$$l_p \leq \phi_p(x_1 \ldots x_n) \leq L_p$$

We shall now explore some analytical techniques of optimization which will enable us to go more or less directly to an optimum solution. The choice of an effective technique depends on which of several possible forms the specific problem actually takes. But before going on, we shall detour into the geometry of the optimization problem.

It will be important to our understanding of the optimization problem to have a geometric visualization of the analytical description. To do so, we will visualize an $n + 1$-dimensional coordinate system in which we can plot the n variables, $x_1 \ldots x_n$, and the criterion value U. Since it is not possible to visualize an $(n + 1)$ hyperspace, we will be satisfied to think of a 3-space and to extend the analysis to the hyperspace. Let x_1 correspond to the usual x axis and x_2 to the y axis. The criterion value, U, will correspond to the z axis. The x_1, x_2 axes will form a *basis plane* over which we will construct the criterion function, $U(x_1, x_2)$. The functional constraint $\psi_1(x_1, x_2) = 0$ will describe a curve on the basis plane. We project this curve upward onto the criterion surface. We now have a curve in space, corresponding to the curve, $\psi_1(x_1, x_2) = 0$; and, at the same time, the curve conforms to the surface $U(x_1, x_2)$. If we visualize ourselves as moving along this space curve, we will rise or fall, depending on the shape of U. If the optimum corresponds to a maximum, we shall seek the highest point as we move on the curve; if to a minimum, then the lowest point as we move on the curve. In either case the x_1, x_2 coordinates of the optimum point will satisfy the constraint ψ_1, since we have followed the projection of its curve on the surface, U.

The same explanation can be extended to the $n + 1$-dimensional space, *sans* the geometric visualization. The values of U are plotted on the $n + 1$ axis, which can be imagined as vertical to an n-dimensional hyperplane, constituting the basis plane. On the hyperplane is plotted a constraint function $\psi_1(x_1 \ldots x_n)$ which forms on it an n-dimensional hypercurve. The latter is projected up to the curved hypersurface, forming on it an $n + 1$-dimensional hypercurve which we can follow until we arrive at an optimum point.

If we had a second functional constraint, $\psi_2(x_1, x_2) = 0$, the two curves corresponding to the two constraints would intersect at a particular point on the basis plane, or possibly at several points. The optimization problem would degenerate, because the constraints would be so tight that the design would be fixed at one of the intersection points irrespective of the criterion. In the case of the n-dimensional problem, ψ_1 and ψ_2 will intersect to form a new hypercurve which will still be on the n-dimensional basis plane. We can visualize this in 3-space. Two curved surfaces (that may be regarded as curves, each with two degrees of freedom, on a 3-dimensional hyperplane) in 3-space will intersect. The line of intersection will form a curve in 3-space (which is still a curve on the 3-dimensional hyperplane, but now has only one degree of freedom). Indeed, we may have any number of functional constraints, ψ_i, up to but not including n. We observe that on the unconstrained basis plane we have n degrees of freedom, that is, from any point on the basis plane we can move arbitrarily with n different orthogonal increments and still remain on the plane. As soon as we specify a constraint function ψ_1, we lose one degree of freedom, that is, from any point on the constraint curve we can only move in $n - 1$ orthogonal increments and still stay on the hypercurve. Finally if we have n

constraint functions, the intersections of these will reduce the degrees of freedom to zero, that is, will fix a particular point, or possibly several distinct points, just as two constraints do on the x_1, x_2 plane. Therefore, the optimization problem degenerates if $m \geq n$, the constraints being too tight then to allow for any design discretion.

Now if we consider the curve on the n-dimensional basis plane, and project it up to the criterion function surface, we shall trace a curve on the latter surface. If we visualize ourselves as moving along the projected curve, we shall rise or fall, depending on the shape of the criterion function surface. If the optimum corresponds to a maximum, we shall seek the highest point as we move on the curve; if to a minimum, the lowest point.

We inquire into the situation when regional constraints are applied. Again we visualize a two-dimensional basis plane. The relation $\phi_1(x_1, x_2)$ represents a family of curves on the x_1, x_2 basis plane. Of this family, one extreme is $\phi_1(x_1, x_2) = L_1$, and the other is $\phi_1(x_1, x_2) = l_1$. The permissible region lies in the area between the two extreme curves and includes points on the curves. By projecting this area up to the criterion function surface, we shall define a region on the surface which we may explore for an optimum. If we introduce a second regional constraint, $l_2 \leq \phi_2(x_1, x_2) \leq L_2$, then another similar area will be defined on the basis plane. The two curved strips of area will intersect on the plane to form a four-sided area, each of the sides being a segment of one of the limiting curves. If this quadrilateral-like area on the basis plane is projected up to the criterion surface, it will map out a closed region on the surface in which it is permissible to seek the optimum. If still another regional constraint is added, we shall have a hexagon-like region to project upon the criterion surface. In general, the number of regional constraints is not limited by theoretical considerations, as the polygon which they form can have many sides. In this respect they differ from functional constraints, whose number we found to be limited to less than the number of relevant variables.

THE LINEAR OPTIMIZATION PROBLEM—LINEAR PROGRAMMING

Although the general optimization problem involves variables in higher order relationships, there is a class of optimization problems occurring frequently in the operation of systems in which the variables are linearly related. The standard form for the linear programming problem includes a linear criterion function U (often called an objective function or a cost function in the general literature on linear programming), and a set of linear regional constraints ϕ as follows:

$$U = k_1x_1 + k_2x_2 + \ldots k_nx_n \rightarrow \text{Minimum}$$

$$\phi_1 = a_{11}x_1 + a_{12}x_2 + \ldots a_{1n}x_n \geq r_1$$

$$\phi_2 = a_{21}x_1 + a_{22}x_2 + \ldots a_{2n}x_n \geq r_2$$

$$\vdots$$

$$\phi_m = a_{m1}x_1 + a_{m2}x_2 + \ldots a_{mn}x_n \geq r_m$$

All of the variables are constrained to be non-negative, that is, $x_i \geq 0$ for all i.

The geometrical visualization of the linear problem is like the more general one, except that the criterion function is now a hyperplane in $n + 1$ space instead of a curved surface, and the regional constraints mark out hyperlines on an n-dimensional basis plane instead of curves. In 3-space, $U = k_1 x_1 + k_2 x_2$ represents an ordinary plane, sloping upward in some way, as determined by the coefficients k_1 and k_2, relative to the basis plane of x_1 and x_2. The regional constraints, for example

$$\phi_j = a_{j1} x_1 + a_{j2} x_2 \geq r_j,$$

represent lines on the x_1, x_2 plane. The stipulation that x_1 and x_2 must be non-negative limits the permissible region to the positive quadrant of the x_1, x_2 basis plane. Therefore, these axes and the set of regional constraints define an open polygon-like figure on the basis plane which we will project upward to the overlying criterion plane. With a little reflection you can see that some one of the corners of the polygon-like figure, when projected onto the criterion plane, must be at a minimum level. This is the answer we are seeking. The area inside and on the boundaries of the open polygon, as drawn on the basis plane does not include the origin, namely $x_1 = 0$, $x_2 = 0$. Therefore if we start at the origin and draw a level line on the criterion surface–a line parallel to the basis plane, we can move this level line parallel to itself (that is, perpendicular to the gradient of the criterion plane) until it makes the first contact with a corner of the open polygon. This corner will define the variables which produce the optimum solution, and its elevation U will be the optimum value. The process is illustrated in Figure 11.1, which shows the allowed region and projections of the level lines of the criterion plane, corresponding to $U = $ constant.

In the actual process of solution, the algebraic form, or *algorithm* as it is called, will first represent the level line at the origin. The level line will

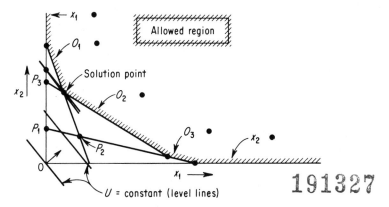

FIG. 11.1 Representation of a Linear Programming Problem.

then move up to the intersection P_1 which is closer to the origin than any of the other possible intersections of the constraint lines. The process tests the tentative point and determines that it is not in the allowable region. Next, the level line moves to P_2 where a similar test indicates that a solution has not yet been attained, as it does also at point P_3. Finally, the next move brings the level line to the solution point. The algebraic process for doing this, which is similar in some respects to solving a set of simultaneous equations, is known as the *simplex method;** it is applicable to problems of n dimensions.

For our purposes it will be useful to present the linear problem in matrix notation.

$$U = KX \rightarrow \text{Minimum}$$

$$\Phi = AX \geq R$$

where: K is the 1 by n row vector $(k_1 \ldots k_n)$

X is the n by 1 column vector $\begin{pmatrix} x_1 \\ \vdots \\ x_n \end{pmatrix}$

A is the m by n matrix $\begin{pmatrix} a_{11} & \ldots & a_{1n} \\ \vdots & & \\ a_{m1} & \ldots & a_{mn} \end{pmatrix}$

R is the m by 1 column vector $\begin{pmatrix} r_1 \\ \vdots \\ r_m \end{pmatrix}$

We will briefly review the few operations for manipulating vectors and matrices which we shall need for the present purpose. A row vector may be multiplied by a column vector. The order of multiplication and the proper correspondence of dimensions is important. For example, in KX we note that the dimensions of K are 1 by n, that is, 1 row by n columns; but for X they are n by 1, meaning n rows by 1 column. The row dimension is given first and the column dimension follows. Multiplication always proceeds from row to column; therefore, a row must always precede a column, and there must be as many columns in the row vector as there are rows in the column vector if the multiplication is to have meaning. This can be checked by noting that the inner dimensions are the same. Thus, in the product KX we have 1 by n times n by 1.

Although A is a matrix, the same rule applies. In the product AX, the dimensional arrangements are m by n times n by 1. Since the inner dimensions are n for both, the multiplication can be performed. It proceeds as

---

* Many texts have been written on linear programming and the simplex technique. One book which is quite complete is Walter W. Garvin, *Introduction to Linear Programming*, (New York: McGraw-Hill Book Company, 1960).

with two vectors:–row by column. Thus the first row of A multiplied with the column vector X will be $a_{11}x_1 + \ldots + a_{1n}x_n$. It is related to the scalar element r_1 by the inequality, $\geq$. The second inequality is obtained from the second row of A and the column vector X, and so on. We observe that the result of multiplying a row vector by a column vector is a scalar quantity–a quantity of one dimension, but the result of multiplying a matrix by a vector is, in general, another vector. Each of the expressions $a_{i1}x_1 + \ldots a_{in}x_n$ is a scalar, since the individual terms can be added together as soon as values are ascribed to the variables. The set of these expressions forms a column of scalars corresponding to a new column vector. However, the dimension of the new column vector is not generally the same as that of the old one. The product of the matrix and the vector involved the dimensions m by n times n by 1. The two n's cancel out, leaving m by 1 as the dimensions of the new vector. In a similar way we may multiply two matrices AB, providing the inner dimensions are equal. Thus m by p times p by n will result in a new matrix C of dimensions m by n. The multiplication is performed row by column exactly as performed for matrix with vector; the C_{ij} element (the element at the intersection of the ith row and the jth column) is formed by multiplying the ith row of A by the jth column of B.

Very frequently in this class of linear problems we are required to maximize revenue or profit or some other criterion. This will generate a problem formulation that is not in the standard form. We may think of such a problem as one in which the revenue is to be maximized while constrained, not to exceed the use of certain maximum specified amounts of scarce input resources, in contrast to the first problem, the standard form, in which cost is minimized, subject to the constraints of meeting certain minimum amounts of required outputs. The two problems are presented in Table 11.1 for comparison. Notice that in the standard problem Φ must be *equal to or more than* the requirements vector R, while in the dual form Φ must be *equal to or less than* the availability vector K. Fortunately, the dual problem can always be converted into the standard form, as will be illustrated in a following example.

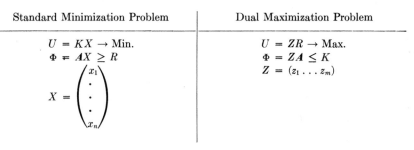

Standard Minimization Problem	Dual Maximization Problem
$U = KX \to$ Min. $\Phi = AX \geq R$ $X = \begin{pmatrix} x_1 \\ \cdot \\ \cdot \\ \cdot \\ x_n \end{pmatrix}$	$U = ZR \to$ Max. $\Phi = ZA \leq K$ $Z = (z_1 \ldots z_m)$

TABLE 11.1

FORMULATION OF THE STANDARD AND DUAL PROBLEMS

AN EXAMPLE OF LINEAR PROGRAMMING IN DESIGN

Linear programming has found wide acceptance in the oil industry as a technique for programming operations. It can also be used as a tool in design, particularly in the early stages that involve feasibility studies and preliminary designs. Consider the example of an oil refinery. It is connected to pipe lines, each carrying a crude oil of a distinctive grade flowing from a different oil field. In the refinery the constituents of the crude oils are first separated by distillation; then some of the heavier fractions are reduced to lighter constituents by cracking; and, finally, the end products are blended to produce an assortment of marketable commodities.* We shall suppose that the plant has already been built. Management has an operating problem, namely, to decide how much of each crude oil to buy and what products to make in order to realize the highest profit each day after considering the prevailing prices. They are constrained by the maximum amounts of each crude oil they are allowed to draw daily from the pipe lines, by the distillation capacity, by the cracking capacity, by the blending and storage capacities, and by the marketing facilities. If we, as designers, have not correctly proportioned the plant with respect to these several kinds of capacity we have unduly restricted the profit potentialities of the refinery. Therefore, we project a sequence of typical operating situations for the refinery, giving each typical situation its proper weight in terms of expected frequency. We can then ask whether, by changing the relative proportions of the proposed refinery, we could improve the annual operating profit. The proportional sizes of the several kinds of capacity become our set of design parameters; the annual operating profit is our design criterion. For each choice of values for the parameters we examine the expected annual operating profits until we have found an optimal set.

In order to carry out the design optimization, we have first to perform the optimization of the refinery operation under typical conditions, assuming that some values have been assigned to the design parameters. Figure 11.2 will help to make the operation clear. It is a highly simplified flow diagram which considers only the distilling and cracking facilities. We assume two crude oil inputs, No. 1 and No. 2. These flow directly to various units in the distillation facility; but here we assume a single path in order to simplify the example. By referring to Table 14.2, we find that an input of one barrel of Crude No. 1 enters the distillation facility and requires one barrel of distilling capacity. (This implies that we need, as an input, one barrel of distilling capacity to service an input of one barrel of Crude No. 1.) The result of this operation is an output of 0.5 bbl. of Intermediate No. 1, 0.3 bbl. of Intermediate No. 2, 0.1 bbl. of Finished Product No. 1, and 0.1 bbl. of Finished Product No. 2. Finally, the cost of a barrel of Crude No. 1 is $1.80. The convention used in the table is

---

* See George B. Dantzig, "Formulating and Solving Linear Programs", in *Modern Mathematics for the Engineer*, ed. Edwin F. Beckenbach (New York: McGraw-Hill Book Company, 1960) pp. 216–22.

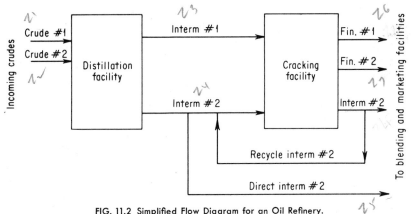

FIG. 11.2 Simplified Flow Diagram for an Oil Refinery.

to show inputs as positive quantities, outputs as negative, costs as negative, and revenues as positive. Crude No. 1 is designated by the variable Z_1. Clearly, if the input is Z_1 barrels of Crude No. 1, the outputs will be proportionally increased, and the cost will be proportionally higher. The limits are shown in the row marked available. Thus the maximum daily delivery of Crude No. 1 is 10,000 bbl.; the daily cracking capacity is 2500 bbl.

Note that some of Intermediate No. 2 is recycled through the cracking facility to break it down to finished products, and some is sold as is. In actual practice the intermediate products are commodities like fuel oil, diesel oil, and stove oil. The market fluctuates; for example, in the winter the demand may be heavy for light fuel oil and relatively light for gasoline, while in summer the situation is reversed.

The problem can now be set down in algebraic form from the data listed in Table 11.2. The variables Z_j have the meanings indicated in the table under the heading, Product.

$$U = -1.8Z_1 - 2.0Z_2 - 0.2Z_3 - 0.3Z_4 + 4Z_5 + 5Z_6 + 6Z_7 \rightarrow \text{Maximum}$$

$$\phi_1 = Z_1 \leq 10,000 \quad \text{(crude 1 capacity)}$$

$$\phi_2 = Z_2 \leq 6,000 \quad \text{(crude 2 capacity)}$$

$$\phi_3 = Z_1 + Z_2 \leq 8,000 \quad \text{(dist capacity)}$$

$$\phi_4 = -0.5Z_1 - 0.5Z_2 + Z_3 \leq 0 \quad \text{(inter #1)}$$

$$\phi_5 = -0.3Z_1 - 0.2Z_2 - 0.4Z_3 + Z_4 + Z_5 \leq 0 \quad \text{(int #2)}$$

$$\phi_6 = Z_3 + Z_4 \leq 2,500 \quad \text{(crackg capacity)}$$

$$\phi_7 = -0.1Z_1 - 0.2Z_2 - 0.2Z_3 - 0.5Z_4 + Z_6 \leq 0 \quad \text{(Fin #1)}$$

$$\phi_8 = -0.1Z_1 - 0.1Z_2 - 0.3Z_3 - 0.4Z_4 + Z_7 \leq 0 \quad \text{(Fin #2)}$$

93

Capacity Factors

Product	Operation	Cru #1	Cru #2	Dist.	Int #1	Int #2	Crack	Fin #1	Fin #2	Unit Costs and Revenues
Crude #1 Z_1	Distilling	1		1	−0.5	−0.3		−0.1	−0.1	−1.8
Crude #2 Z_2			1	1	−0.5	−0.2		−0.2	−0.1	−2.0
Interm #1 Z_3	Cracking				1	−0.4	1	−0.2	−0.3	−0.2
Interm #2 Z_4						1	1	−0.5	−0.4	−0.3
Interm #2 Z_5						1				4.0
Fin #1 Z_6	Marketing							1		5.0
Fin #2 Z_7									1	6.0
Available		10,000	6,000	8,000			2,500			

TABLE 11.2

OPERATING DATA FOR A HIGHLY-SIMPLIFIED REFINERY OPERATION

The criterion function U is the gross operating profit, obtained by adding costs and revenues with due regard to signs. Thus $-0.3Z_4$ reflects the cost of cracking Z_4 barrels of Intermediate No. 2 at \$0.30 per bbl. regardless of whether the Intermediate No. 2 came directly from the distillation facility or whether it was recycled from the cracking facility. Of the regional constraints, ϕ_1 expresses the fact that Z_1 may not exceed the daily allowable input of 10,000 bbl. of Crude No. 1; ϕ_2 has a similar expression. Then ϕ_3 provides that the combined input of Z_1 and Z_2 may not exceed the daily distillation capacity of 8,000 bbl. The constraints ϕ_4 and ϕ_5 show the origins and material balances for Intermediates No. 1 and No. 2. For example, Z_5 is the quantity of Intermediate No. 2 which is sold directly, and Z_4 the amount which is cracked into lighter fractions; the total $Z_4 + Z_5$ is accounted for entirely by $-0.3Z_1$ and $-0.2Z_2$ distilled from Crudes No. 1 and No. 2 respectively and by $-0.4Z_3$, the amount resulting from cracking Intermediate No. 1. In like manner ϕ_6 represents the fact that the total of Z_3 and Z_4, which is to be cracked, may not exceed the cracking capacity of 2,500 bbl. Finally ϕ_7 and ϕ_8 represent the sources and outputs of Finished Products No. 1 and No. 2. You may note that the coefficients of each constraint and of the criterion function are the column entries of the table.

The formulation we now have is that of the dual problem. It must be transformed to the standard form. To do so we note from Table 11.1 that $U = ZR$. Accordingly we obtain the elements of the vector R by taking the coefficients in $U = ZR$. Thus, R is the column vector, $(-1.8, -2.0, -0.2, -0.3, 4, 5, 6)$. We show it in row form merely to conserve space; identifying it as a column vector precludes confusion. By the same token we identify the vector K in the equation, $\Phi = ZA \le K$ as the row vector, $(10{,}000, 6{,}000, 8{,}000, 0, 0, 2{,}500, 0, 0)$. We have left the determination of the matrix A. We remember that in $\Phi = ZA$, Z is a row vector; it is multiplied by each column of A to produce $\phi_1 \ldots \phi_m$. Thus

$$\phi_1 = a_{11}Z_1 + a_{21}Z_2 + \ldots + a_{71}Z_7 \le k_1.$$

If we examine ϕ_1 we see that the coefficients are $(1, 0, 0, 0, 0, 0, 0)$. This is the first column of A. In this way we can get the remaining columns.

The matrix A is then

1	0	1	-0.5	-0.3	0	-0.1	-0.1
0	1	1	-0.5	-0.2	0	-0.2	-0.1
0	0	0	1	-0.4	1	-0.2	-0.3
0	0	0	0	1	1	-0.5	-0.4
0	0	0	0	1	0	0	0
0	0	0	0	0	0	1	0
0	0	0	0	0	0	0	1

We can now formulate the standard problem by using the column vector X instead of the original row vector Z and obtaining the form shown in Table 11.1.

We have now to demonstrate how to obtain the solution for the standard form by using the simplex algorithm. The solution is developed in Tables 11.3–11.10. Observe that the matrix A is posted in the upper portion of the initial tableau. The rows are preceded by the captions $A1$ to $A7$; the columns are headed by $B1$ to $B8$. In this particular case the matrix A is 7 by 8. In the last column, headed O/I (Outputs and Inputs) post the

	$B1$	$B2$	$B3$	$B4$	$B5$	$B6$	$B7$	$B8$	O/I
$A1$	1	0	1	-0.5	-0.3	0	-0.1	-0.1	1.8
$A2$	0	1	1	-0.5	-0.2	0	-0.2	-0.1	2.0
$A3$	0	0	0	1	-0.4	1	-0.2	-0.3	0.2
$A4$	0	0	0	0	1	1	-0.5	-0.4	0.3
$A5$	0	0	0	0	1	0	0	0	-4
$A6$	0	0	0	0	0	0	1	0	-5
$A7$	0	0	0	0	0	0	0	①	-6
$B1$	1								
$B2$		1							
$B3$			1						
$B4$				1					
$B5$					1				
$B6$						1			
$B7$							1		
$B8$								1	
K	10,000	6,000	8,000	0	0	2,500	0	0	0

TABLE 11.3

SIMPLEX ALGORITHM. INITIAL TABLEAU OF THE STANDARD FORM OF THE OIL REFINERY PROBLEM

column vector $-R$, which is 1 by 7. This array fully occupies the first 7 rows of the tableau. The next 8 rows are headed by captions $B1$ to $B8$. Here we enter the basis matrix which reflects the condition that the column vector $X = (x_1 \ldots x_8)$ is constrained to the non-negative coordinate space; thus we have the set of inequalities, $x_1 \geq 0 \ldots x_8 \geq 0$. As in the case of the matrix A presented above, we can write this latter set as $BX \geq 0$, where B is the unit matrix (ones on the diagonal and zeros elsewhere). The corresponding column vector of zeros is posted under O/I. It will be generally expedient to omit the actual entry of zeros, the blank space being sufficient to indicate a zero. Finally the last row, with the caption K contains the 1 by 8 row vector K.

The transition from the initial tableau to the second is accomplished by the sequence of operations which are described in the following list.

(1)–In general, designate the cell lying at the intersection of the ith row and the jth column as Q_{ij}.

96

	B1	B2	B3	B4	B5	B6	B7	A7	O/I
A1	1		1	−0.5	−0.3	0	−0.1	−0.1	1.2
A2		1	1	−0.5	−0.2	0	−0.2	−0.1	1.4
A3				1	−0.4	1	−0.2	−0.3	−1.6
A4					1	1	−0.5	−0.4	−2.1
A5					1			0	−4
A6							①	0	−5
A7								1	0 ←
B1	1								
B2		1							
B3			1						
B4				1					
B5					1				
B6						1			
B7							1		
B8								1	6
K	10,000	6,000	8,000	0	0	2,500	0	0	0

TABLE 11.4

SIMPLEX ALGORITHM. SECOND TABLEAU

↓

	B1	B2	B3	B4	B5	B6	A6	A7	O/I
A1	1		1	−0.5	−0.3		−0.1	−0.1	0.7
A2		1	1	−0.5	−0.2		−0.2	−0.1	0.4
A3				1	−0.4	1	−0.2	−0.3	−2.6
A4					①	1	−0.5	−0.4	−4.6
A5					1				−4
A6							1		0 ←
A7								1	0
B1	1								
B2		1							
B3			1						
B4				1					
B5					1				
B6						1			
B7							1		5
B8								1	6
K	10,000	6,000	8,000	0	0	2,500	0	0	0

TABLE 11.5

SIMPLEX ALGORITHM. THIRD TABLEAU

↓

	B1	B2	B3	B4	A4	B6	A6	A7	O/I
A1	1		1	−0.5	−0.3	0.3	−0.25	−0.22	−0.68
A2		1	1	−0.5	−0.2	0.2	−0.3	−0.18	−0.52
A3				①	−0.4	1.4	−0.4	−0.46	−4.44
A4					1				0 ←
A6					1	−1	0.5	0.4	0.6
A6							1		0
A7								1	0
B1	1								
B2		1							
B3			1						
B4				1					
B5					1	−1	0.5	0.4	4.6
B6						1			
B7							1		5
B8								1	6
K	10,000	6,000	8,000	0	0	2,500	0	0	0

TABLE 11.6

SIMPLEX ALGORITHM. FOURTH TABLEAU

↓

	B1	B2	B3	A3	A4	B6	A6	A7	O/I
A1	1		1	−0.5	−0.5	(1.0)	−0.45	−0.45	−2.9
A2		1	1	−0.5	−0.4	0.9	−0.5	−0.41	−2.74
A3				1					0 ←
A4					1				0
A5					1	−1	0.5	0.4	0.6
A6							1		0
A7								1	0
B1	1								
B2		1							
B3			1						
B4				1	0.4	−1.4	0.4	0.46	4.44
B5					1	−1	0.5	0.4	4.6
B6						1			
B7							1		5
B8								1	6
K	10,000	6,000	8,000	0	0	2,500	0	0	0

TABLE 11.7

SIMPLEX ALGORITHM. FIFTH TABLEAU

	B1	B2	B3	A3	A4	A1	A6	A7	O/I	
A1						1			0	←
A2	−0.9	1	0.10	−0.05	0.05	0.90	−0.09	0	−0.13	
A3				1					0	
A4					1				0	
A5	1		1	−0.5	(0.5)	−1	0.05	−0.05	−2.3	
A6							1		0	
A7								1	0	
B1	1									
B2		1								
B3			1							
B4	1.4		1.4	0.3	−0.3	−1.4	−0.23	−0.17	0.38	
B5	1		1	−0.5	0.5	−1	0.05	−0.05	1.7	
B6	−1		−1	0.5	0.5	1	0.45	0.45	2.9	
B7							1		5	
B8								1	6	
K	7,500	6,000	5,500	1,250	1,250	2,500	1,125	1,125	7,250	

TABLE 11.8

SIMPLEX ALGORITHM. SIXTH TABLEAU

↓

	B1	B2	B3	A3	A5	A1	A6	A7	O/I	
A1						1			0	
A2	−1	1	0	0	0.10	1	−0.10	0	0.10	
A3				1					0	
A4	−2		−2	1	2	2	−0.10	0.10	4.6	
A5				1					0	←
A6							1		0	
A7								1	0	
B1	1									
B2		1								
B3			1							
B4	2		②	0	−0.6	−2	−0.20	−0.20	−1.0	
B5	0		0	0	1	0	0	0	4.0	
B6	−2		−2	1	1	2	0.40	0.50	5.2	
B7							1		5	
B8								1	6	
K	5,000	6,000	3,000	2,500	2,500	5,000	1,000	1,250	13,000	

TABLE 11.9

SIMPLEX ALGORITHM. SEVENTH TABLEAU

↓

	B1	B2	B4	A3	A5	A1	A6	A7	O/I
A1						1			0
A2	−1	1			0.10	1	−0.10	0	0.10
A3				1					0
A4	0		−1	1	1.4	0	−0.30	−0.10	2.6
A5					1				0
A6							1		0
A7									0
B1	1								
B2		1							
B3	−1		0.5		0.3	1	0.10	0.10	0.50
B4			1						
B5					1				4.0
B6	0		−1	1	0.4		0.20	0.30	4.2
B7							1		5
B8								1	6
K	3,000	6,000	1,500	2,500	3,400	8,000	1,300	1,550	14,500

TABLE 11.10

SIMPLEX ALGORITHM. SOLUTION OF THE OIL REFINERY PROBLEM

(2)–In the O/I column, among the negative entries find the one that has the largest absolute magnitude. (Remember that it was $-R$ which was entered under O/I.) Designate this row as the pth row.

(3)–Divide each entry in the pth row by the corresponding entry in the K row. However, do not change the numbers in either row. Select the largest quotient and designate its column as the sth column. Its cell, that is Q_{ps} will be designated the pivot cell. Draw a circle around it.

(4)–Prepare a second tableau with column and row headings exactly like the preceding one, except replace the s *column heading* by the p *row caption.*

(5)–Hereafter, refer to cells in the preceding tableau with the letter Q and to cells in the new tableau with the letter N. Thus the general cell Q_{ij} in the old tableau becomes N_{ij} in the new one. Divide the values in the pivot column, namely in the cells Q_{is}, by the value in the pivot cell, Q_{ps}. Enter the results into the corresponding N_{is} cells. Thus $N_{is} = Q_{is}/Q_{ps}$. The entry in N_{ps} will clearly be one. In all that follows, the K row and the O/I column are to be treated in the same way as any other row or column in the tableau.

(6)–In all of the cells in the pivot row, except the pivot cell, enter zeros; thus $N_{pj} = 0$ for all j except s, and $N_{ps} = 1$.

(7)–Enter values in all of the remaining cells by using the general formula $N_{ij} = Q_{ij} - N_{is} \cdot Q_{pj}$. You are to understand that the values in the cells are used in the formula. You will find it convenient to work by rows.

(8)–In the new tableau, examine the O/I column. If all of the entries in this column are zero or positive the solution tableau has been obtained. If not, again select from the negative values the one with the largest absolute magnitude (the most negative entry) and repeat the operations, thereby developing a new tableau.

(9)–Continue with the procedure until a solution tableau is reached.

We have now to interpret the solution tableau of Table 11.10. If our original problem had been a standard minimization one, then the solution would be X equal to the column vector $(0, 0, 0.5, 0, 4, 4.2, 5, 6)$, namely, the vector appearing in the O/I column in the rows $B1 \ldots B8$. The criterion value would be $U = 14{,}500$ in the cell of row K and column O/I.

However, in this example we had the dual, maximization problem. The Z vector is found in the K row. We recall that some of the column headings have changed from B to A. The columns headed A contain elements of the Z vector; in particular the $A1$ column contains z_1, and so on. The columns which still have B headings represent zero values for Z elements. Thus taking the values from the K row we have $Z = (8{,}000; 0; 2{,}500; 0; 3{,}400; 1{,}300; 1{,}500)$. The criterion value is still found in the cell of the K row, O/I column and is $U = 14{,}500$.

The significance of the solution is as follows. For the stated conditions the optimum operation results if 8,000 bbl. of Crude No. 1 $(z_1 = 8{,}000)$ are purchased for the day's run, and none of Crude No. 2 $(z_2 = 0)$. Although 4,000 bbl. of Intermediate No. 1 will be produced, only 2,500 bbl. can be cracked $(z_3 = 2{,}500)$. Because this product has no immediate market, the excess 1,500 bbl. would have to be dumped or stored (or sold somewhere for a very low price). None of the Intermediate No. 2 will be cracked $(z_4 = 0)$. All of the Intermediate No. 2, produced by distillation of the crude and by cracking Intermediate No. 1 $(z_5 = 3{,}400)$ will be sold. All of Finished Products No. 1 and No. 2 produced from distillation of Crude No. 1 and from cracking Intermediate No. 1 $(z_6 = 1{,}300, z_7 = 1{,}550)$ will be sold. The resulting gross operating profit will be $14,500. Under the stated conditions and prices, any other mode of operation will yield a lower operating profit.

In this short exposition we have been unable to discuss some of the subtleties. Among these are questions of degeneracy, handling of mixed inequalities, parametric linear programming, and the treatment of some types of non-linear problems by linear approximations. With respect to mixed inequalities, the matter can usually be resolved by changing signs. For example, $5 + 2 > 6$; by changing signs the inequality is reversed. Thus multiplying both sides by -1, we obtain $-5 - 2 < 6$.

Of particular interest in design is the extension to parametric linear programming. Essentially this is a sensitivity-type of analysis, showing which parameter, if changed, will produce the greatest effect on the criterion value. In the oil refinery example we would like to know whether reducing the distillation capacity or increasing the cracking capacity will have the greater effect on the operating profit. With only two design parameters the question can be easily resolved; but when many design parameters come into play, the answers are not obvious.*

METHOD OF STEEPEST DESCENT

The general non-linear optimization problem can sometimes be reduced to a statement of a criterion function only. This can be done when the optimization is not subject to regional constraints and the functional constraints are simple in form so that they may be substituted directly into the criterion function. The problem is then to explore the modified criterion surface $U = U(x_1 \ldots x_n)$ for the highest peak or deepest valley depending on which extreme value is optimal. The method of exploration begins at some convenient starting point, preferably as close to the solution point as we can guess. We might imagine standing at the starting point, and by surveying the terrain, choose the direction of steepest slope, the *gradient*, and follow this direction downward (or upward if we seek a maximum) for some convenient distance. We then resurvey the terrain from the new location, determine the direction of the gradient and repeat until the gradient attains an absolute magnitude of zero. At this point we are presumably at the minimum—that point at the bottom of a valley—providing that the surface was of simple contour. At least three things can happen to contravene a true solution:—one, the valley may actually be a local depression, and the true solution would be at the bottom of some other deeper valley; two, the point may be on a ledge, and further travel in the same direction would continue the downward trend; three, the location may be on a saddlepoint, and further travel in some orthogonal direction would continue the downward path. This process of exploration is well-suited to computer adaptation, for the gradient at any starting point can be approximated by numerical methods, a new point located at a given increment from the old one and so on. When the surface is suspected to contain several valleys, a suitable statistical design can be applied to the choice of starting points, the region of interest being explored and the optimum finally selected from the set of extreme values.

We have now to consider the answers to two questions:—first, how to determine the direction of steepest descent; second, how to estimate the proper distance to move in a given direction before stopping to re-establish a new orientation. Again we visualize the criterion surface and imagine a level contour. Such a contour will correspond to $U(x_1 \ldots x_n) = $ constant, the value of the constant depending on the elevation above the basis plane. Arbitrarily selecting a point on the contour, we can slice into the surface in each of the orthogonal directions corresponding to $x_1 \ldots x_n$ (the axes of

---

* Garvin, *Linear Programming*, previously cited, has a chapter on parametric linear programming.

the basis plane). In each of these directions, say the ith one, the slope is $\partial U/\partial X_i$. Each of these individual slopes are the components, lying in their respective orthogonal directions, of a vector called the gradient and designated ∇U (read del U or gradient U). The gradient, being the resultant of the component slopes, will have a direction determined by the individual magnitudes. The direction of the gradient will be the direction of steepest slope; the magnitude of the gradient will be the steepest slope. As with any vector we can resolve it into components in various directions. In particular the component orthogonal to it vanishes (in 2- or 3-space it would be at a right angle), which means that the slope in the orthogonal direction is zero. But this is the level contour, for its slope is by definition equal to zero. Thus the gradient is at every point normal to the level contour at that point. To state the foregoing formally, we write:

$$\nabla U = \left(\frac{\partial U}{\partial x_1} \ldots \frac{\partial U}{\partial x_n}\right)$$

$$\text{Magnitude } \nabla U = \left[\left(\frac{\partial U}{\partial x_1}\right)^2 + \ldots + \left(\frac{\partial U}{\partial x_n}\right)^2\right]^{1/2}$$

We now have the answer to the first question. If we lay out the components, $\partial U/\partial x_i$, on the basis plane, this will be the direction of ∇U. In practical terms, the ratios of the increments along the x_i and x_j axes are adjusted so that

$$\frac{\Delta x_i}{\Delta x_j} = \frac{\partial U/\partial x_i}{\partial U/\partial x_j}$$

Problems of any considerable size are impractical to do by hand, and must be prepared for automatic computation. A digital computer can be programmed to obtain approximations of partial derivatives by using differences (refer to Chapter 10). By using the increment corresponding to the largest derivative as a base value, the other increments are found as fractions from the ratios of the derivatives. If our starting point is $X_0 = x_{10} \ldots x_{n0}$, we will obtain $(\partial U/\partial x_1)_0 \ldots (\partial U/\partial x_n)_0$ by substituting the values of the starting coordinates into the general expressions for the partial derivatives. Subsequent points will be numbered with increasing subscripts for identification.

Given the direction of the gradient at the starting point, how far should we move out on it for the most effective result. Let us imagine cutting out a thin slice of the surface along the gradient. If $U(x_1 \ldots x_n)$ has a finite minimum, then the slice along the initial gradient must have a finite minimum which, generally, will not be as deep. Let y, a positive quantity, be distance along the gradient. We would like to make y such that $dU/dy = 0$, which means moving along the direction of the gradient until we reach a relative minimum*. Any further travel in that direction will cause U to increase. We will take the component of y in the direction of x_i as $\Delta x_i = -y(\partial U/\partial x_i)_0$. Accordingly $x_i = x_{i0} - y(\partial U/\partial x_i)$. Now we substitute for each x_i in $U(x_1 \ldots x_n)$ the corresponding value in terms of y. The result is that U equals a function of the coordinates of the starting point, the gradient at the starting point, and the single variable y. This is of great interest for computer use, for it converts a multidimensional problem into one of a single variable y. Now we can set to zero the derivative $dU/dy = 0$, solve for y and calculate a new set of coordinates to serve as a fresh starting point†. Let y_k represent the kth trial, then the new set of coordinates will be

$$x_{ik} = x_{ik-1} - y_k(\partial U/\partial x_i)_{k-1}$$

The process is continued until the partial derivatives $(\partial U/\partial x_i)$ for all i are approximately equal to zero. This will be a tentative optimum:– whether it is a true optimum must be determined by certain tests.

AN APPLICATION OF THE METHOD OF STEEPEST DESCENT

We illustrate the foregoing steepest descent method with the example of the power transmission problem developed in Chapter 10. We have

$$U = 21.9 \cdot 10^7 E^{-2} C^{-1} + 3.9 \cdot 10^6 C + 10^3 E \to \text{Minimum}$$

$$\phi_1 = 63.5 C^{1/2}(8.52 - \ln C) - E \geq 0,$$

The modified criterion function is obtained by replacing I with its equivalent value in terms of E as specified by $\psi_1 = \sqrt{3} EI - K_1 = 0$. If we omit the regional constraint ϕ_1 by asserting that we will make the conductors hollow and large enough in diameter to avoid corona discharge, we will have an unconstrained criterion function; therefore, we may apply the method of steepest descent†.

We will choose as the coordinates of our starting point X_0 the values $E_0 = 100$ kv and $C = 0.10$ mho.

We find the general expressions for the partial derivatives as:

$$\partial U/\partial E = -43.8 \cdot 10^7 E^{-3} C^{-1} + 10^3$$

$$\partial U/\partial C = -21.9 \cdot 10^7 E^{-2} C^{-2} + 3.9 \cdot 10^6$$

After we have located the kth point, the values of the coordinates in

---

* $dU/dy = 0$ is generally an equation of higher order in y. Therefore there will be more than one root. The required solution for y is usually the real root with smallest absolute magnitude.

† We omit the constraint on critical voltage in order to simplify the illustration.

the neighborhood of that point will be

$$E = E_k - y(\partial U/\partial E)_k$$

$$C = C_k - y(\partial U/\partial C)_k$$

Taking the derivatives of E and C, we get

$$(dE/dy)_k = -(\partial U/\partial E)_k$$

and

$$(dC/dy)_k = -(\partial U/\partial C)_k$$

We need the derivative of U with y in the neighborhood of the kth point.
$4.56 \cdot 10^{-5} \, dU/dy$

$$= 2[C_k - y(\partial U/\partial C)_k]^{-1} \cdot [E_k - y(\partial U/\partial E)_k]^{-3}(\partial U/\partial E)_k$$

$$+ [C_k - y(\partial U/\partial C)_k]^{-2} \cdot [E_k - y(\partial U/\partial E)_k]^{-2}(\partial U/\partial C)_k$$

$$- 1.78 \cdot 10^{-2}(\partial U/\partial C)_k - 4.57 \cdot 10^{-6}(\partial U/\partial E)_k$$

$$= 0$$

At any stage, all of the terms will have known numerical values. Therefore we can solve by numerical approximation for the value of y_{k+1} and C_{k+1}.

The starting point $k = 0$, is at E_0, C_0 where the partial derivatives are

$$(\partial U/\partial E)_0 = -3.38 \cdot 10^3; \quad (\partial U/\partial C)_0 = 1.71 \cdot 10^6$$

k Trial	E_k kv	C_k mho	y	$(\partial U/\partial E)_k$ $/kv	$(\partial U/\partial C)_k$ $/mho	U $10^5
0	100	0.10		$-3.38 \cdot 10^3$	$1.71 \cdot 10^6$	7.09
1	100	0.075	$1.46 \cdot 10^{-8}$	$-4.85 \cdot 10^3$	0	6.84
2	143	0.075	$0.89 \cdot 10^{-2}$	0	$2.55 \cdot 10^6$	5.79
3	143	0.051	$0.94 \cdot 10^{-8}$	$-1.94 \cdot 10^3$	0	5.52
4	205	0.051	$3.19 \cdot 10^{-2}$	0	$1.91 \cdot 10^6$	5.07
5	205	0.037	$0.73 \cdot 10^{-8}$	$-0.39 \cdot 10^3$	0	4.91
6	229	0.037	$6.15 \cdot 10^{-2}$	0	$0.85 \cdot 10^6$	4.87
7	229	0.033	$0.05 \cdot 10^{-8}$	$-0.11 \cdot 10^3$	0	4.84
8	238	0.033	$8.15 \cdot 10^{-2}$	0	$0.35 \cdot 10^6$	4.84
9	238	0.0315	$0.03 \cdot 10^{-8}$	$-0.06 \cdot 10^3$	0	4.84
10	241	0.0315	5.0	0	$-0.1 \cdot 10^6$	4.84
11	241	0.0311	$0.04 \cdot 10^{-8}$	$-0.01 \cdot 10^3$	0	4.84
12	242	0.0311	$10.0 \cdot 10^{-2}$	0	0	4.84

TABLE 11.11

STEEPEST DESCENT SOLUTION FOR POWER TRANSMISSION LINE PROBLEM

We take $E_1 = 100 + 3.38 \cdot 10^3 y$ and $C_1 = 0.10 - 1.71 \cdot 10^6 y$. Upon substituting these expressions into dU/dy above we obtain, except for terms of negligible size,*

$$(0.10 - 1.71 \cdot 10^6 y)^{-2} \cdot 100^{-2} = 1.78 \cdot 10^{-2}$$

From this $y = 1.46 \cdot 10^{-8}$ and

$$E_1 = 100 + 5.10^{-5} = 100$$

$$C_1 = 0.10 - 0.025 = 0.075$$

The results of successive trials are listed in Table 11.11. The solution is obtained at $k = 12$; it is $E = 242$ kv, $C = 0.0311$ mho, giving an optimum value for the criterion of $\$4.84 \cdot 10^5$.

TEST FOR A TRUE EXTREME

We have now to test whether or not we have reached a true extreme point or only a relative one. We consider the curvature at the solution point; in particular we want the curvatures corresponding to surface sections in the several coordinate directions. If these curvatures are heterogeneous (some positive and some negative), then the solution is at a saddle point and is not a true extremum, for the implication is that in some directions the surface curves upward and in others downward. The curvature is related to the second derivative; indeed, for a plane curve it is $R = (d^2U/dx^2)[1 + (dU/dx)^2]^{-3/2}$ and since $dU/dx = 0$ at a stationary point, the radius of curvature is simply equal to the second derivative. By sketching a curve with a minimum and making a rough plot of the slope, it will be clear that if $d^2U/dx^2 \equiv U_{xx} > 0$, the curve will have a minimum; and if $U_{xx} < 0$, it will have a maximum. By analogy, at the solution point of a multidimensional problem if some of the second partial derivatives $U_{x_i x_i}$ are positive and some negative, then we are at a saddle point. However, it may be that the ridge of the saddle sweeps upward narrowly in a direction between the coordinate axes; therefore, the curvature being homogeneous in sign is not enough to insure a true minimum. Some relations among the mixed partial derivatives $U_{x_i x_j}$ must be satisfied. Let $a_{ij} = U_{x_i x_j}$ be the numerical values of the second partial derivatives at the solution point. Form the matrix of second partial derivatives

$$\begin{pmatrix} a_{11} & \cdots & a_{1n} \\ \vdots & & \vdots \\ a_{n1} & \cdots & a_{nn} \end{pmatrix}$$

---

* Although the equation is of the 5th order, the incremental increase in E is small, i.e., $E_1 = E_0 - y(\partial U/\partial E)_0 \approx E_0$. Therefore the equation reduces to quadratic.

From the matrix form the n determinants

$$D_1 \equiv a_{11} \qquad D_2 \equiv \begin{vmatrix} a_{11}a_{12} \\ a_{21}a_{22} \end{vmatrix} \qquad D_3 \equiv \begin{vmatrix} a_{11}a_{12}a_{13} \\ a_{21}a_{22}a_{23} \\ a_{31}a_{32}a_{33} \end{vmatrix}$$

and so on. If $D_k > 0$ for all k from one to n, then the solution point is not a saddle point and is probably a true minimum, or, if all of the unequalities are reversed, a true maximum, unless it is on a ledge or horizontal inflection point. In this rather unlikely situation, third order or higher partial derivatives need to be examined. Although we may have established the solution point as a true minimum, we may still not be sure that it is an absolute minimum, unless the form of the surface or the physical conditions are such as to preclude other, or deeper minima. If there is substantial doubt that the absolute minimum has been found, then we must resort to a statistical exploration.

We illustrate the use of the test in the preceding power transmission line example.

$$U_{EE} = 131.4 \cdot 10^7 E^{-4} C^{-1}$$

$$U_{CC} = 43.8 \cdot 10^7 E^{-2} C^{-3}$$

$$U_{EC} = 43.8 \cdot 10^7 E^{-3} C^{-2}$$

Substituting the numerical values at the solution point: $a_{EE} = 12.3$, $a_{CC} = 2.5 \cdot 10^8$, $a_{EC} = 3.2 \cdot 10^4$.
We form the matrix

$$\begin{pmatrix} 12.3 & 3.2 \cdot 10^4 \\ 3.2 \cdot 10^4 & 2.5 \cdot 10^8 \end{pmatrix}.$$

Then:

$$D_1 = 12.3 > 0$$

$$D_2 = 12.3 \cdot 2.5 \cdot 10^8 - 3.2^2 \cdot 10^8 = 20.5 \cdot 10^8 > 0$$

The test shows, with the exceptions noted before, that the solution is a true minimum.

OPTIMIZATION UNDER FUNCTIONAL CONSTRAINTS

For solving optimization problems involving functional constraints, which are implicit functions of the design parameters and other variables, we will need a general and powerful method of attack. We can proceed by using Lagrangian multipliers. We have the criterion function U and the functional constraints $\psi_1 \ldots \psi_m$, functions of the n variables $x_1 \ldots x_n$. In general, $m < n$; therefore, if we can find $n - m$ additional equations, we can fix values for the n variables. The condition that U shall be an extremum is

$$dU = \sum_{i=1}^{n} (\partial U/\partial x_i) \, dx_i = 0$$

Noting that each of the $\psi_j = 0$, we can write the differentials in the neighborhood of the extremum as

$$d\psi_1 = \sum_{i=1}^{n} (\partial \psi_1/\partial x_i) \, dx_i = 0$$

$$\vdots$$

$$d\psi_m = \sum_{i=1}^{n} (\psi_m/\partial x_i) \, dx_i = 0$$

We multiply each of the latter equations by a Langrangian multiplier, thus for the jth equation we have typically:

$$\lambda_j \, d\psi_j = \sum_{i=1}^{n} \lambda_j(\partial \psi_j/\partial x_i) \, dx_i = 0$$

Adding all of the equations and consolidating the terms, we get

$$\sum_{i=1}^{n} \left[\partial U/x_i + \lambda_1(\partial \psi_1/\partial x_i) + \ldots + \lambda_m(\partial \psi_m/\partial x_i)\right] dx_i = 0$$

However, each of the differentials dx_i are arbitrary and independent of each other; therefore each bracketed term must be equal to zero in order to insure the above equality. As a result we now have n equations of the form

$$(\partial U/\partial x_i) + \lambda_1(\partial \psi_1/\partial x_i) + \ldots + \lambda_m(\partial \psi_m/\partial x_i) = 0$$

We observe that we have the n new equations and the m original functions, $\psi_1 \ldots \psi_m$. We have added only m undetermined multipliers which, when added to the original n variables, gives us $(n + m)$ unknowns. But happily we have $(n + m)$ equations which should allow us to eliminate the λ_j and still provide n equations to fix n original variables. Since we have prescribed them for $dU = 0$, the values so determined must correspond to some sort of an extremum.

We will at first confine our efforts to the n new equations. We consider the partial derivatives $(\partial \psi_m/\partial x_j)$ as coefficients $\lambda_1 \ldots \lambda_m$ as our variables and proceed to eliminate the latter. Since these are *linear* equations, we can accomplish the elimination by the usual Cramer's rule using determinants. However, we are here dealing with partial derivatives, so it is convenient to use the Jacobian notation. We will need only the first m of the n new equations. For these we can construct the square matrix,

	ψ_1 $\quad\cdots\quad$ ψ_m	
x_1	$(\partial\psi_1/\partial x_1)$	$(\partial\psi_m/\partial x_1)$
$\vdots$		
x_m	$(\partial\psi_1/\partial x_m)$	$(\partial\psi_m/\partial x_m)$

The general entry in the kj cell is $(\partial\psi_j/\partial x_k)$. We note that every possible derivative is represented in the matrix. The Jacobian of the set of functions $\psi_1 \ldots \psi_m$, relative to the first m variables $x_1 \ldots x_m$ is defined as the determinant of the square matrix set out in the foregoing.

We shall briefly review how a determinant is developed when the matrix is given. We shall start with the upper left hand entry $(\partial\psi_1/\partial x_1)$, and multiply it by a new determinant called a minor. The minor is formed from all of the entries contained in a smaller matrix that comprises all of the original rows and columns except the row and column containing the original entry. We need not have started with the upper left hand entry; we could have taken any one arbitrarily. However, the sign has to be adjusted according to the location of the lead element. With k denoting the row number and j the column number, the sign is computed as $(-1)^{k+j}$. Thus for the upper left hand corner choice, both k and j are one. Hence, the sign is positive. A minor, given its correct sign, is called a cofactor. We must make m lead choices, which we can do by taking every element in the row, or, alternatively, every element in the column. We will prefer to choose the elements in the row. Let the notation D^i_{kj} denote the cofactor formed with the kj as the lead element and the superscript i indicating the rank of the cofactor (the rank of the full determinant will be assumed to be m for the purpose of this explanation, which means that the full determinant may not equal zero). Thus the first expansion is

$$(\partial\psi_1/\partial x_1)\, D^{m-1}_{11} - (\partial\psi_2/\partial x_1)\, D^{m-1}_{12} + \ldots + (-1)^{1+m}(\partial\psi_m/\partial x_1)\, D^{m-1}_{1m}$$

In turn each of the cofactors can be expanded in the same way, treating each as if it were an original determinant. A determinant has a scalar value which can be computed numerically when all of the coefficients have assigned values. The Jacobian of the matrix ensemble is written and defined as

$$J\left(\frac{\psi_1 \ldots \psi_m}{x_1 \ldots x_m}\right) = D^m$$

As an illustration, given $\psi_1(x_1, x_2)$ and $\psi_2(x_1, x_2)$, the Jacobian is

$$J\left(\frac{\psi_1\psi_2}{x_1x_2}\right) = \frac{\partial\psi_1}{\partial x_1}\cdot\frac{\partial\psi_2}{\partial x_2} - \frac{\partial\psi_2}{\partial x_1}\cdot\frac{\partial\psi_1}{\partial x_2}$$

109

If $\psi_1 = \sin x_1 \cos x_2$ and $\psi_2 = \cos x_1 \sin x_2$, then:

$$J\left(\frac{\psi_1 \psi_2}{x_1 x_2}\right) = (\cos x_1 \cos x_2)^2 - (\sin x_1 \sin x_2)^2$$

We illustrate the use of Cramer's rule in solving simultaneous equations. For example:

$$a_{11}\lambda_1 + a_{12}\lambda_2 = b_1$$

$$a_{12}\lambda_1 + a_{22}\lambda_2 = b_2$$

Then

$$\lambda_1 = \begin{vmatrix} b_1 & a_{12} \\ b_2 & a_{22} \end{vmatrix} \div \begin{vmatrix} a_{11} & a_{12} \\ a_{21} & a_{22} \end{vmatrix} ; \quad \lambda_2 = \begin{vmatrix} a_{11} & b_1 \\ a_{21} & b_2 \end{vmatrix} \div \begin{vmatrix} a_{11} & a_{12} \\ a_{21} & a_{22} \end{vmatrix}$$

Note especially that the denominator is the determinant of the coefficient matrix, but that the determinant in the numerator is formed by replacing the coefficients of λ_k by the b_k (that is, in solving for λ_k we replace a_{kj} by b_k in the numerator).

We are now ready to solve for and eliminate the λ_k in the set of equations involving the $\psi_1 \ldots \psi_m$. We transpose the $\partial U/\partial x_k$ to the right hand side so that it can play the same role as the b_k in the simultaneous equations above. The typical equation of the set is

$$(\partial\psi_1/\partial x_k)\lambda_1 + \ldots + (\partial\psi_m/\partial x_k)\lambda_m = -(\partial U/\partial x_1)$$

where k ranges from 1 to m. The solution for the typical λ_k is

$$\lambda_k = -J\left(\frac{\psi_1 \ldots U \ldots \psi_m}{x_1 \ldots x_k \ldots x_m}\right) \div J\left(\frac{\psi_1 \ldots \psi_m}{x_1 \ldots x_m}\right)$$

Note that here, just as in the preceding simple example $-(\partial U/\partial x_i)$ replaces $(\partial\psi_k/\partial x_i)$ in the numerator when solving for λ_k. The replacement must be in the kth column or the result will have an incorrect sign. This is indicated by placing U above the kth position in the Jacobian. One necessary provision is that

$$J\left(\frac{\psi_1 \ldots \psi_m}{x_1 \ldots x_m}\right) \neq 0,$$

that is, the determinant has the rank m; otherwise λ_k has no useful solution.

By the process above, we are able to solve for every λ_k. However, of the n derived equations we have only used the first m to find the λ_k. We substitute these values into the remaining $n - m$ equations, thereby eliminating the λ_k. Of the last $n - m$ equations consider the rth one as typical. Writing it more compactly by using the summation sign, we have

$$\sum_{k=1}^{m} (\partial\psi_k/\partial x_r)\lambda_k = -(\partial U/\partial x_r)$$

where $m < r \leq n$.

Substituting the new value for λ_k, the rth equation becomes:

$$\sum_{k=1}^{m} (\partial\psi_k/\partial x_r) \cdot -J\binom{\psi_1 \ldots U \ldots \psi_m}{x_1 \ldots x_k \ldots x_m} \div J\binom{\psi_1 \ldots \psi_m}{x_1 \ldots x_m} = -(\partial U/\partial x_r)$$

Transposing, we finally have

$$\sum_{k=1}^{m} (\partial\psi_k/\partial x_r) \cdot J\binom{\psi_1 \ldots U \ldots \psi_m}{x_1 \ldots x_k \ldots x_m} = (\partial U/\partial x_r) \cdot J\binom{\psi_1 \ldots \psi_m}{x_1 \ldots x_m}$$

where $r = m + 1 \ldots n$.

We may observe that in each typical equation the Jacobian is multiplied by a partial derivative involving x_r. We shall consider these derivatives as the lead terms of an expansion of a matrix one order higher than the original one. How this might come to pass we can see by imagining a matrix like the original one, but with an added row to take care of x_r and an added column into which the displaced ψ_k is shifted. Thus, the original matrix represented by the Jacobian

$$J\binom{\psi_1 \ldots \psi_k \ldots \psi_n}{x_1 \ldots x_k \ldots x_n}$$

is increased by one order to become

$$J\binom{\psi_1 \ldots U \ldots \psi_n\psi_k}{x_1 \ldots x_k \ldots x_n\psi_r}$$

In expanding the latter matrix we draw the lead terms from the rth row.

By assuming such an expansion we will achieve a great simplification. One obstacle, however, is that the partials of U are not in a fixed column, but take on successive positions from 1 to m. Another obstacle is that the signs of the Jacobians are all positive. To be correct cofactors they should alternate in sign according to the rule $(-1)^{1+k}$. Actually, by overcoming the first obstacle we will automatically overcome the second one. If we move U from one column to the adjacent one, we will change the sign from positive to negative. If we move the U to the first position in each of the Jacobians of the summation, the signs will alternate, since each successive Jacobian involves moving U one column less than the preceding Jacobian; consequently, we can combine the cofactors with the lead elements to construct a Jacobian of one higher order. It will be

$$J\binom{U\psi_1 \ldots \psi_m}{x_rx_1 \ldots x_m} = 0,$$

and there will be one such for every r in the set $r = m + 1 \ldots n$.

We can demonstrate the composition more easily by showing the reverse process, that of expanding the complete Jacobian into cofactors. If we do, using the first row for the lead elements and recognizing that ψ_k is now in the $k + 1$ column, because the first column is occupied by U:

$$\sum_{k=1}^{m} (\partial\psi_k/\partial x_r) \cdot (-1)^{2+k} \cdot J\left(\frac{U\psi_1 \ldots \psi_{k-1}\psi_{k+1} \ldots \psi_m}{x_1 \ldots x_m}\right)$$

$$+ (\partial U/\partial x_r) \cdot J\left(\frac{\psi_1 \ldots \psi_m}{x_1 \ldots x_m}\right) = 0$$

Moving $Uk_2 - 1$ columns to the kth position, we change the sign according to $(-1)^{k-1}$. Thus every sign is changed from $(-1)^{2+k}$ to $(-1)^{2+k} \cdot (-1)^{k-1}$ or to $(-1)^{1+2k}$. Clearly, the exponent must be odd no matter what integer value k assumes. Therefore, all of the signs become negative and we have the original equation with which we started. If the foregoing is not clear, form the matrix of

$$J\left(\frac{U\psi_1 \ldots \psi_m}{x_r x_1 \ldots x_m}\right)$$

expand into cofactors using the first row (the x_r row) as the lead elements, move the U column of the kth cofactor to the kth position adjusting signs accordingly, and compare with the original equation.

The solution point must now satisfy the following equations:

$$\psi_1(x_1 \ldots x_n) = 0$$
$$\vdots$$
$$\psi_m(x_1 \ldots x_n) = 0$$

$$\psi_{m+1} = J\left(\frac{\psi_1 \ldots \psi_m U}{x_1 \ldots x_m x_{m+1}}\right) = 0$$

$$\vdots$$

$$\psi_n = J\left(\frac{\psi_1 \ldots \psi_m U}{x_1 \ldots x_m x_n}\right) = 0$$

The n equations fix the coordinates $x_1 \ldots x_n$ of the extrema on the criterion surface in $n + 1$ space. Note, however, that each Jacobian involves only $m + 1$ of the n variables.

AN APPLICATION OF THE METHOD OF LAGRANGIAN MULTIPLIERS

The power transmission line problem will serve to illustrate the Lagrangian method of undetermined multipliers. We recall that

$$U = 3 \cdot 10^{-3} I^2 C^{-1} + i(3k_2 C + k_3 E) \rightarrow \text{Minimum}$$

$$\psi_1 = \sqrt{3}EI - K_1 = 0$$

Again, we omit the regional constraint ϕ_1. We find it convenient to set up the matrix of partial derivatives.

	ψ_1	U
I	$\sqrt{3}E$	$-6 \cdot 10^{-3}k_1IC^{-1}$
C	0	$3 \cdot 10^{-3}k_1I^2C^{-2} - 3ik_2$
E	$\sqrt{3}I$	$-ik_3/K_2$

We now assemble the set of simultaneous equations and divide out extraneous factors.

$$\psi(EIC) = \sqrt{3}EI - K_1 = 0 \tag{1}$$

$$J\left(\frac{\psi_1 U}{IC}\right) = 10^{-3}k_1I^2C^{-2} - ik_2 = 0 \tag{2}$$

$$J\left(\frac{\psi_1 U}{IE}\right) = ik_3E + 6\cdot 10^{-3}k_1I^2C^{-1} = 0 \tag{3}$$

We have three design parameters and three equations which fix their values to yield the optimum. From equations (2) and (3) we get

$$I = \left(\frac{10^3 ik_2}{k_1}\right)^{1/2}C$$

$$I^2 = \left(\frac{10^3 ik_3}{6k_1}\right)EC$$

Dividing one by the other to eliminate C, we have

$$I = \frac{k_3}{6}\left(\frac{10^3 i}{k_2 k_1}\right)^{1/2}E$$

Eliminating I by using equation (1), we have finally

$$E^2 = \frac{6K_1}{k_3}\left(\frac{k_2 k_1}{3 \cdot 10^3 i}\right)^{1/2}$$

Using the numerical values for the constants from the power transmission line example in Chapter 10 we obtain $E = 242$ kv, $I = 120$ amp, and $C = 0.0311$ mho, which agree with the results obtained by the steepest descent method. The test for a true extremum may be applied as explained in the preceding section.

THE NEWTON-RAPHSON APPROXIMATION METHOD

Although the use of Lagrangian multipliers produces in principle a solution of the general optimization problem with functional constraints, the resulting set of nonlinear simultaneous equations can present a formidable challenge in the reduction to numerical solutions. In the example of the preceding section we were able to move to a solution in a straightforward manner because we could develop explicit relations for some of the variables; thereby they were eliminated from other equations. But often, especially in large complicated problems, the variables are so implicitly enmeshed in each other that their direct explication is impossible. We face the situation where the optimal solution is contained implicitly in the set of n equations, and where we must find some way to extract the coordinates of the solution point.

The Newton-Raphson* method deals directly with the set of functions $\psi_1 \ldots \psi_n$. Let Ψ be the vector whose n components are the individual functions ψ_i. We assume as the initial starting point the vector X_0. By adding an incremental vector ΔX we will arrive at a new point $X_0 + \Delta X$. We wish to move as close to the solution point $\Psi = 0$ as possible. To get an approximation for ΔX we make a Taylor's expansion in the neighborhood of X_0, and equate the resulting expression for Ψ to zero, solve for ΔX, and finally calculate $X_1 = X_0 + \Delta X$.

To perform the foregoing operations, we first suppose that we have found the νth approximation, X_ν, at which point Ψ has the value Ψ_ν. The Taylor expansion around X_ν is

$$\Psi = \Psi_\nu + \Delta X (\Psi')_\nu + \epsilon_2^2 + \epsilon_3^3 + \ldots$$

In the equation above, Ψ_ν is a vector whose components are the specific values of the functions ψ_i at the point X_ν, and $(\Psi')_\nu$ is the matrix formed of all possible first partial derivatives using the specific values they have at X_ν.

We set $\Psi = 0$, neglect the higher order terms, and solve for X. We find first

$$\Psi_\nu = -\Delta X (\Psi')_\nu.$$

We must remember that we are dealing with a matrix. Previously we defined the rules for matrix multiplication. However, although the operation inverse to multiplication is not simple division, it is possible to show, under suitable circumstances, that for a matrix A, a unique *inverse matrix* A^{-1} can be found such that $AA^{-1} = (1)$, where the matrix (1) is the unit matrix of the same order as A. The unit matrix is defined as the one having its diagonal elements equal to one and all others equal to zero. The inverse of a matrix is found by a process similar to the one used in solving a set of simultaneous linear equations. You may refer to the many standard texts which describe the process.†

If we multiply both sides of the equation for ΔX by the inverse matrix,

---

* See F. B. Hildebrand, *Introduction to Numerical Analysis*, (New York:–McGraw-Hill Book Company, Inc., 1956) pp. 447–51.

† For example, I. S. Sokolnikoff and R. M. Redheffer, *Mathematics of Physics and Modern Engineering*, (New York: McGraw-Hill Book Company, Inc., 1958) pp. 332–3.

$(\mathbf{\Psi}')_\nu^{-1}$, we obtain ΔX explicitly as

$$\Delta X = -\mathbf{\Psi}_\nu (\mathbf{\Psi}')_\nu^{-1}$$

This leads to the recurrence relation

$$X_{\nu+1} = X_\nu - \mathbf{\Psi}_\nu (\mathbf{\Psi}')_\nu^{-1}$$

We note that the product of the row vector $\mathbf{\Psi}_\nu$ and the matrix $(\mathbf{\Psi}')_\nu$ is another row vector whose components are not easily expressed in ordinary algebraic form. However, the numerical computations are not difficult. Computers are especially able to handle, with permanently programmed subroutines, the inversion and multiplication of large matrices.

AN EXAMPLE INVOLVING SIMULTANEOUS NONLINEAR EQUATIONS IN OPTIMIZATION

We use the bearing problem of Chapter 10 to illustrate how to apply the Newton-Raphson method in solving the set of nonlinear equations that are obtained when the criterion function is reduced by the method of Lagrangian multipliers. The design of a component, shown schematically in Figure 11.3 includes among other desiderata, both high torsional rigidity of the journal and low frictional resistance in the bearings. Increasing the size of the journal will reduce the torsional flexure but, at the same time, will increase the friction loss. Therefore, we cannot minimize both simultaneously. We can set limits on one and optimize the other; or we can set relative values on each desideratum and construct a composite criterion function. We shall choose the latter approach.

We will assume for the present that forced lubrication is adequate to

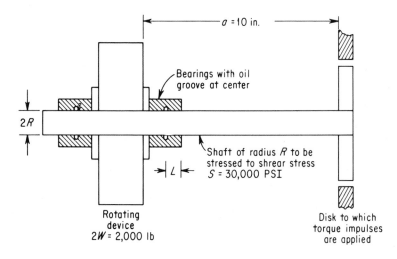

FIG. 11.3 Schematic Representation of Bearing Problem.

115

hold the rise in oil temperature to a fixed increment, and that external cooling is adjusted so that the oil in the bearing is at a predetermined operating temperature; hence, we shall say that, for the given oil, the viscosity μ is fixed at 10^{-6} lb sec per sq in. The load on the bearing and the speed of rotation are set by the design requirements of the subsystem, and are respectively $W = 1,000$ lb, and $w = 100$ radians per sec. The design parameters are the radius of the journal R and the half length of the bearing L. We will fix the expected value of the clearance C at 0.001 in. to satisfy production conditions. The eccentricity variable ϵ appears implicitly; its value depends on the other design parameters. However, to avoid excessive wear from fine dirt particles in the lubricant, and to preclude the possibility of metal to metal contact, we will require an oil film thickness of not less than $h_0 = 10^{-4}$ in. at the minimum point. This fixes the value of ϵ according to the relation $1 - \epsilon = h_0/C$ at $\epsilon = 0.90$.

The free length of the journal, between the flywheel-like mass and the drive point, is $a = 10$ in. The driving torque is applied as a series of impulses. Their intensity and frequency are adjusted to keep the device rotating within specified limits of rotational velocity. The shaft is of steel, heat-treated to a tensile strength of 120,000 psi. A limit of 30,000 psi is placed on maximum shear stress S. The shear modulus of elasticity is $E_S = 12 \cdot 10^6$ psi. The angle of twist is related to the mechanical properties of the material, the geometry of the shaft and the dynamic torque T, which arises when a driving impulse is applied. However, it is more convenient to use the shear stress corresponding to the torque. In terms of shear stress the angle of twist is

$$\theta = \frac{aS}{E_S} \cdot \frac{1}{R} \text{ radians}$$

The frictional moment is, from Chapter 10, for the two bearings

$$M = \frac{8\pi}{\sqrt{1 - \epsilon^2}} \frac{\mu w}{C} \cdot R^3 L \text{ in. lb}$$

The criterion function expresses the idea of minimizing a properly weighted combination of twist and friction. Thus

$$U = m_1 M + m_2 \theta \rightarrow \text{Min.}$$

where m_1 and m_2 are coefficients of relative importance. In evaluating the relative importance of these two factors in respect to the design objectives of the whole component, we shall make the value judgment that each 0.005 radians of twist is worth as much as 2 in. lb of frictional torque. Accordingly

$$U = \frac{1}{2}M + \frac{1}{0.005}\theta \rightarrow \text{Min.}$$

Now we can write the description of the bearing and journal performance

116

relevant to the criterion, which is

$$U = \frac{4\pi}{\sqrt{1 - \epsilon^2}} \frac{\mu w}{C} R^3 L + \frac{200 a S}{E_S} \cdot \frac{1}{R} \to \text{Min.}$$

$$\psi_1 = 2W - \frac{uw}{C^2} RL^3 P'(\epsilon) = 0$$

$$\psi_2 = h_0 - C(1 - \epsilon) = 0$$

$$\psi_3 = S - 30{,}000 = 0$$

The equations reflect the following considerations:

$\psi_1 = 0$ constrains the design parameters to values which will support W (see Chapter 10); $\psi_2 = 0$ represents the necessary conditions for preserving the minimum oil film thickness, h_0; and $\psi_3 = 0$ represents the constraint on shear stress.

By substituting the specified numerical values for the given terms and eliminating S and ϵ by using ψ_2 and ψ_3 in U and ψ_1, we obtain as a specific archetype

$$U = 2.9R^3L + 5R^{-1} \to \text{Min.}$$

$$\psi_1 = RL^3 - 0.207 = 0$$

We set up the matrix of first partial derivatives in order to derive the set of simultaneous equations which define the optimum point.

	ψ_1	U
R	L^3	$8.7R^2L - 5R^{-2}$
L	$3RL^2$	$2.9R^3$

The resulting set of equations, ($\psi_1 = 0$ from the original set of constraints, and ψ_2 from the matrix above) after cancelling extraneous factors, is

$$\psi_1 = RL^3 - 0.207 = 0$$

$$\psi_2 = J\left(\frac{\psi_1 U}{RL}\right) = 23.2R^4L - 15 = 0$$

For the Newton-Raphson method the recurrence relation is

$$X_{\nu+1} = X_\nu - \Psi_\nu(\Psi')_\nu^{-1}$$

in which the subscript indicates the trial number in the succession of approximations.

The vector Ψ is (ψ_1, ψ_2). We form the matrix (Ψ') by using the first partial derivatives of Ψ:

	ψ_1	ψ_2
R	$\psi_{1R} = L^3$	$\psi_{2R} = 92.8R^3L$
L	$\psi_{1L} = 3RL^2$	$\psi_{2L} = 23.2R^4$

In the table ψ_{1R} stands for $\partial\psi_1/\partial R$, and so on.

We must now set up the inverse matrix $(\Psi')_p^{-1}$. To do so, first find the determinant of (Ψ'). This is

$$| \Psi' | = 23.2R^4L^3 - 278.4R^4L^3 = -255.2R^4L^3$$

Next modify the matrix (Ψ') by replacing each term by its corresponding cofactor (see Page 109). Then transpose the resulting matrix by literally rotating it on its diagonal. Finally, multiply the modified matrix by the reciprocal of the determinant. This forms the inverse matrix. For a two by two matrix, the cofactors are single terms and the inverse is

$$\begin{pmatrix} \psi_{1R} & \psi_{2R} \\ \psi_{1L} & \psi_{2L} \end{pmatrix}^{-1} = \frac{1}{\psi_{1R}\psi_{2L} - \psi_{2R}\psi_{1L}} \cdot \begin{pmatrix} \psi_{2L} & -\psi_{2R} \\ \psi_{1L} & \psi_{1R} \end{pmatrix}$$

For the matrix presently being considered, the inverse is

$$(\Psi')^{-1} = -\frac{1}{255.2R^4L^3} \begin{pmatrix} 23.2R^4 & -92.8R^3L \\ -3RL^2 & L^3 \end{pmatrix}$$

$$= \begin{pmatrix} -0.0909L^{-3} & 0.364R^{-1}L^{-2} \\ 0.0118R^{-3}L^{-1} & -0.00392R^{-4} \end{pmatrix}$$

The incremental values are obtained by multiplying (ψ_1, ψ_2) by the above matrix.

$$\Delta R = \psi_1(-0.0909L^{-3}) + \psi_2(0.0118R^{-3}L^{-1})$$

$$\Delta L = \psi_1(0.364R^{-1}L^{-2}) + \psi_2(-0.00392R^{-4})$$

Introduce the terms for ψ_1 and ψ_2 and obtain the recursive formulae

$$R_{\nu+1} = R_\nu - R_\nu(0.183R - 0.177R^{-3}L^{-1} + 0.0188R^{-3}L^{-1})$$

$$L_{\nu+1} = L_\nu - L_\nu(0.273L - 0.0755R^{-1}L^{-2} + 0.0588R^{-4})$$

The computations are listed in Table 11.12. Note that the columns are numbered, and that the column numbers are used in the headings in such a way as to indicate automatically the computation to be made without reference to the formulae. This same type of planning is required in preparing a problem for an electronic computer, the column headings becoming the addresses where the evolving information is stored. Actually the table operates on the original expressions for the functions and the derivatives: thus

$$R_{\nu+1} = R_\nu + R_\nu\left(\frac{\psi_1\psi_{2L} - \psi_2\psi_{1L}}{\psi_{1R}\psi_{2L} - \psi_{2R}\psi_{1L}}\right)$$

$$L_{\nu+1} = L_\nu + L_\nu\left(\frac{-\psi_1\psi_{2R} + \psi_2\psi_{1R}}{\psi_{1R}\psi_{2L} - \psi_{2R}\psi_{1L}}\right)$$

118

Starting with the values $R_0 = 1$, $L_0 = 1$, we find

$$R_1 = 1 - (0.183 - 0.177 + 0.0188) = 0.975$$

$$L_1 = 1 - (0.273 - 0.0755 + 0.0588) = 0.744$$

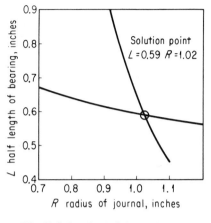

FIG. 11.4 Graphical Solution for Bearing Problem.

The tabular computations converge after five iterations to $R_5 = 1.019$ and $L_5 = 0.592$. For this particular problem we could have used simpler algebraic methods because the variables turned out to be separable. For example, we could have solved for R in ψ_1 and substituted the result in ψ_2, thereby making it a polynomial in L only. We can also solve the equations graphically; this is shown in Figure 11.4.

The combination of values for the design parameters which we have obtained will meet the functional constraints set forth in the design relative to load, speed, oil viscosity, minimum oil film thickness and stress; at the same time, under the conditions of the design criterion this design will yield the highest performance. Other combinations of design parameters can also meet the requirements for safe bearing operation, but the resulting performance, as measured by the assumed criterion function, will be poorer.

OPTIMIZING UNDER REGIONAL CONSTRAINTS

So far we have dealt with the question of regional constraints only in the case of the linear optimization problem (linear programming). Techniques for other cases are being actively investigated under the general heading of nonlinear programming. Several such methods have appeared in current literature.*

To summarize: in this chapter we have developed some of the methods for finding an optimal set of design parameters. We began with the proper mathematical archetype of the proposed design. We translated the performance criteria into a mathematical criterion function. The functional relationships among the design parameters, which reflected the behavior of the object under design, were contributed by the mathematical archetype; they became the functional constraints. Constraints imposed upon the design, usually by the need for compatibility with other coacting members of the system and the system environment, or by specifications on

---

* For example, see C. W. Carroll, "The Created Response Surface Technique", Operations Research, March–April 1961, pp. 169 ff.

Table 11.12
Work Sheet for Bearing Optimization

1	2	3	4	5	6	7	8	9	10	11	12
							(3)(5)	23.2(8)	(9)−15	(2)(7)	(11)−.207
ν	R_ν	L_ν	R^3	R^4	L^2	ψ_{1R} L^3			ψ_2		ψ_1
0	1	1	1	1	1	1	1	23.2	8.2	1	0.793
1	0.975	0.744	0.925	0.900	0.619	0.487	0.710	16.5	1.5	0.475	0.268
2	1.00	0.675	1	1	0.455	0.308	0.675	15.7	0.70	0.308	0.101
3	1.018	0.617	1.06	1.08	0.381	0.235	0.666	15.5	0.50	0.239	0.032
4	1.021	0.600	1.07	1.09	0.360	0.216	0.654	15.2	0.20	0.221	0.014
5	1.019	0.592	1.06	1.08	0.350	0.208	0.641	14.9	0.10	0.212	0.005

1	13	14	15	16	17	18	19	20	21	22	23
	(3)(4)	92.8(13)	(2)(6)	3(15)	23.2(5)	(7)(17)	(14)(16)	(18)−(19)	(12)(17)	(10)(16)	(21)−(22)
ν		ψ_{2R}		ψ_{1L}	ψ_{2L}			D			
0	1	92.8	1	3	23.2	23.2	278	−255	18.3	24.6	−6.3
1	0.727	67.5	0.604	1.81	20.9	10.2	122	−112	5.6	2.72	2.88
2	0.675	62.5	0.455	1.36	23.2	7.15	85.2	−78	2.34	0.95	1.39
3	0.654	60.5	0.388	1.16	25.0	5.88	70.1	−64.2	0.800	0.58	0.22
4	0.642	59.5	0.368	1.10	25.3	5.47	65.5	−60.0	0.354	0.22	0.13
5	0.628	58	0.357	1.07	25.1	5.23	62	−58	0.125	0.11	0.015

1	24	25	26	27	28	29	30	31	32	33	34
	(23)/(20)	(2)(24)	(10)(7)	(12)(14)	(26)-(27)	(28)/(20)	(3)(29)	(2)-(25)	(3)-(30)		
		ΔR					ΔL	$R_{\nu+1}$	$L_{\nu+1}$	R^{-1}	U
0	0.025	0.025	8.2	73.5	-65.3	0.256	0.256	0.975	0.744	1	7.9
1	-0.026	-0.025	0.73	18.1	-17.4	0.143	0.112	1.00	0.675	1.025	7.12
2	-0.018	-0.018	0.21	6.3	-6.1	0.078	0.058	1.018	0.617	1	6.96
3	-0.003	-0.003	0.12	1.94	-1.82	0.028	0.017	1.021	0.600	0.982	6.81
4	0.002	0.002	0.043	0.83	-0.79	0.013	0.008	1.019	0.592	0.981	6.75
5	0	0	0.021	0.29	-0.027	0.0005	0	1.019	0.592	0.981	6.73

input and output variables, formed the regional constraints. By employing Lagrangian multipliers, the criterion function was replaced by nonlinear equations which, together with the original functional constraints, formed a set of simultaneous equations whose solution was the minimum point of the criterion function. The Newton-Raphson method was used to deal directly with the set of simultaneous equations.

chapter

12 | A CASE STUDY

In this last chapter the object will be to illustrate the methodology and some of the theory in carrying out a design project. The case is drawn from my personal experience on a consulting assignment several years ago. It comprises a Feasibility Study and Preliminary Design of an aluminum dross recovery plant. To conserve space, I shall excerpt from the original report just sufficiently to maintain a reasonable continuity in presentation. In doing so, I must omit some of the important practical considerations which played an important role in the study. Comments are added at the end of each section to highlight the application of the Morphology and other materials that were treated in the text.

LETTER OF TRANSMITTAL

Mr. ABC, President
XYZ Company
Los Angeles, California

Dear Sir:

With this letter I submit a report according to your request . . . based on a plant with a normal capacity of 1000 tons of aluminum melt dross, using material with a metallic aluminum content ranging from 10 to 22 percent. The output . . . will be about 150 tons of aluminum ingot per month.

At prevailing prices . . . at rated capacity, the economic study indicates a profit, before interest on loans and state and federal income taxes, of $15,000 per month on a gross volume of sales of $60,000 per month.

The work force . . . on a standard one-shift basis at rated capacity is 14 employees. The expected payroll, including 20 percent for benefits, is about $7,000 per month. The cost of producing the ingot, . . . except interest, is 15 cents per pound. Of this the cost of conversion is $4\frac{1}{4}$ cents per pound. The break-even point is at 50 tons of ingot per month, one-third of rated capacity.

The required capital for fixed facilities, excluding land but including all improvements, is . . . $228,000. Of this, $84,000 is for building and improvements, docks and spur tracks, and $144,000 for equipment. Working capital, to carry one month's supply of raw material inventory and one month of ingot production, requires $75,000.

A layout is included . . . important specifications are developed in detail. The computations, descriptions, and discussions in the body of the report and in the five sets of work sheets should enable a qualified engineer to complete a detailed design of the plant.

The goal of this study was to develop a high profit potential subject to the constraints of the market, permissible investments, and community sanctions. In order to achieve this goal, two major objectives were emphasized in the design, namely to reduce labor as far as was practical and to develop as smooth a flow of material as possible.

Yours truly,

Morris Asimow
Registered Professional Engineer,
California ME 1246

Comments: In this instance the letter serves a dual function: first, as a letter of transmittal which orients the reader to the general situation and sets down the original instructions to the engineer, second, as a summary of the more important objectives, results, and conclusions of the study.

TABLE OF CONTENTS

5. The Plant–Major Equipment, Cost, and Layout
6. Work Force when Operating at Rated Capacity
7. Cost of Manufacture, Projected Profit, and Conditions of Break-Even
8. Work Sheets
   No. 1. Design of Facilities for Handling and Storing Raw Dross
   No. 2. Design of Loading and Unloading Docks
   No. 3. Analysis of Crushing and Grinding Equipment
   No. 4. Preliminary Design of Furnace
   No. 5. Preliminary Design of Casting Machine

1. PURPOSE OF THE REPORT

The purpose . . . is to make an economic study and a preliminary design of a plant to be situated in the Southern California area for recovering aluminum from melt dross and skimmings. These waste products originate . . . in

(a) manufacturing aluminum bars, strips, and extrusions
(b) secondary smelting
(c) aluminum founding and die casting.

The sources are . . . within the Los Angeles industrial area, although under favorable conditions . . . materials from other West Coast areas may be processed.

Comments: The original request was in the form of a primitive statement of need that was phrased essentially as follows:–*we believe that a dross recovery plant is needed in the Los Angeles area.* The problem situation is recognized and some of its elements are stated.

2. NEED FOR A DROSS RECOVERY PLANT IN SOUTHERN CALIFORNIA

The need . . . is based on considerations of economy, customer relations, and availability of locally generated . . . dross. Foremost, . . . , is the cost of transportation.

(a) To obtain one ton of aluminum, five to ten tons of dross must be transported. At 20 dollars per ton of freight, the cost of freight per pound of net aluminum is five to ten cents . . . to midwestern plants. These costs compare with one to two cents per pound . . . to a local plant.

(b) The Los Angeles industrial area affords a large market for aluminum pig. Consequently, selling . . . presents no unusual problems. Freight expense will be small.

(c) Some customers prefer to handle their dross through toll agreements. The customer pays . . . to have his dross converted to aluminum . . . for his own reuse. Freight costs, coming and going, are important. Also questions about metallic contents . . . are easier to monitor and negotiate at close range. Thus proximity ... is an advantage to a prospective toll customer.

(d) Some drosses of unknown quality are purchased subject to later determination of metallic content. Questions arise ... proximity is an important aid in maintaining good relations.

(e) Proximity of the supply market ... reduces inventories by ... control over the rate of delivery. The savings ... are threefold: firstly, in working capital tied up in actual inventory; secondly, in fixed capital ... in storage facilities; and thirdly, in loss owing to oxidation of metallic aluminum.

(f) A substantial supply of ... dross can be obtained from the many local aluminum foundries. The dross production of a single foundry seldom warrants shipments by rail. A local plant can service ... by truck, thus eliminating double handling through waste dealers.

(g) The Los Angeles industrial area is a heavy aluminum consumption area. In converting aluminum pig to extrusion billets, rolling billets, foundry ingots, and to commercial castings, large quantities of dross are produced. Excepting a few small converters, ... is shipped to middle western plants ... uneconomic for an area ... as large as Los Angeles.

Comments: The above statements are the conclusions resulting from the needs analysis. The validity of the need, and also its future potential, are considered.

3. GENERAL STATEMENT OF PLANT REQUIREMENTS

(a) *Capacity.* The proposed plant is based on a normal capacity of processing 1000 tons of dross per month ... expected production of 150 tons of pig ... is reasonable in relation to current supplies. However, ... with the industrial growth ... of this area ... the proposed capacity will become inadequate. Therefore the site and the plant layout should permit expansion.

(b) *Location.* The location should be outside Los Angeles County ... stringent requirements of the Los Angeles Air Pollution Control District anywhere in the county. The crushing and grinding of aluminum dross are very dusty operations. Even in favorable locations adequate measures must be taken to avoid public nuisance.

(c) *Space Requirements.* About 10,000 square feet of working space under roof is required. Light corrugated metal construction will suffice. Additional paved area ... is indicated in the layout. Sufficient ground space ... for waste disposal and future expansion ... necessitates about 5 acres.

(d) *Receiving Capacity.* Receiving capacity ... peak requirement of 3 boxcars per day (Work sheets No. 2). The layout of ... docks and spur tracks ... accommodate 3 boxcars.

(e) *Unloading Facilities.* Dross is shipped in boxcars ... divided be-

125

tween the two ends with bulkheads stopping off the material at the doors. A power scoop can enter and discharge the load into cube-shaped, corrugated, skidded containers about 4 feet on a side. (Work Sheet No. 1.) Each container will hold 3000 pounds of dross . . . 20 of these will be required to store a 60,000-pound carload.

(f) *Preparation Capacity.* By preparation capacity is meant the capability of crushing, grinding, and concentrating dross to essential raw metallic aluminum content. The output product . . . is identified as concentrate. Two basic factors . . . are required.

1. Equipment for crushing, grinding, screening, separating, and handling . . . physically large enough to handle the many large agglomerations.

2. Should have sufficient throughput capacity to reduce operator time . . ., to reduce . . . volume of raw dross to be stored.

(g) *Concentrate Storage Capacity.* Concentrate . . . occupies about 10 percent of original volume. Fewer containers and much less space . . . to accommodate . . . inventory of concentrates. Concentrates . . . segregated with respect to suppliers . . . and quality . . . control is facilitated.

(h) *Melting Capacity.* The concentrates are refined and brought to a suitable chemical composition by melting in a reverberatory furnace (Work Sheet No. 4). Because of the dirty condition of concentrates . . . is best introduced via an open well into which the material is puddled. The well is an extension of the furnace . . . and separated from the interior by a partition wall with openings at the bottom . . . . To produce 150 tons of pig per month requires a melting capacity of 16,000 pounds per day. For an 8 hour working period and a 16 hour holding period per day, judgment indicates a desirable rate of 3000 pounds per hour . . . makes allowance for skimming, alloying, and refining.

(i) *Pig Casting Capacity.* The pig casting machine is . . . expensive capital equipment . . . cost increases rapidly with size. However, inadequate capacity will frequently necessitate holding over the pouring crew at premium wage costs. A minimum size is 3000 pounds per hour. The desirability of a larger machine must be determined by balancing labor costs against capital outlay.

(j) *Waste Disposal.* Disposal of waste . . . is a serious problem . . . at rated capacity 1250 cubic yards per month. From the standpoint of economy . . . dispose . . . at the plant site. An abandoned quarry, or a large pit . . . for fill . . . . Over a 10 year period . . . 150,000 cubic yards . . . requiring a pit of 3 acres and 30 feet deep. Lacking a pit, the waste may be heaped in a mound, flat on top.

(k) *Water Requirements.* Requirements are small, but important. The uses of water are for (a) personnel use, (2) cooling of ingot molds, and (3) dust collecting systems. The plant should have access to a normal water supply. The alternative is to truck water in.

(l) *Power Requirements.* Requirements . . . of 250 kilowatts connected load ... may be wired for 220 or 440 volts. For the latter ... capital outlay is less. If distant from a power network ... a Diesel generator set ... which would be costly compared to purchased power.

(m) *Fuel Requirements.* Most desirable is natural gas ... clean, easily controlled, requires no inventory or storage facility. The site should preferably have access to a normal supply ... 4500 cubic feet per working hour is required (Work Sheet No. 4). A standby supply of 4000 gallons of fuel ... required for shut off periods during cold spells ... when higher priority users make greater demands. The standby suffices for 2 weeks without replenishment. The alternative ... oil all the year round.

(n) *Transportation Facilities.* Of the total incoming material 80 to 90 percent will ... come in by rail ... the remainder by truck. The site should be accessible by rail and highway.

(o) *Dust Controls.* Dust arises in the preparation processes. To avoid public nuisance, equipment ... must be properly hooded and vented to dust filters or precipitators. Cyclones will be adequate ... if not too near a community.

Comment: This section is based mainly on an activity analysis. Taken into account are the required outputs, the undesired outputs such as dust and waste, the provided inputs such as fuel, power, and raw material, environmental inputs such as cause oxidation of the metal, the constraints, quantitative and qualitative on the outputs, the inputs, and the plant and its site. Included, in order to give the report continuity, are some of the results deriving from the preliminary design, particularly from some of the work sheets. Such intermingling is often necessary to make a report convincing. The design criterion expresses the economics of the operation. It is to maximize the profit. The design problem is to design a plant subject to the quantitative and qualitative constraints set forth in this section that will maximize annual profit over a period of about 10 years.

4. GENERAL DESIGN CONCEPT

(A) *Character of Incoming Material.* Incoming dross ... of various sizes of agglomerated aluminum drippings, encased and embedded in cakes, blocks, or rough chunks of non-metallic materials, principally aluminum oxide admixed with fluxing salts, abraded refractories, clay washes, and other foreign materials. Occasional pieces of steel ... in the dross. Size of material ... ranges from dust to chunks two feet in diameter. Aluminum globules ... covered with a coarse layer of oxide ... the active salts in the dross react chemically with the aluminum ... deterioration occurs ... accelerated in wet weather.

(B) *Storage of Raw and Semi-Processed Inventory.* The analysis in Work Sheet No. 1 favors immediate processing and storing concentrates in boxes, alternative (d), . . . the advantages are:

(1) Requires the least capital investment.
(2) Involves the least handling cost by eliminating double handling and excessive in-plant travel distance.
(3) Permits the easiest and most accurate method of controlling inventory and establishing metallic content for remittances.
(4) Minimizes down-grading of metallic content by exposure to weather and passage of time.
(5) Requires least storage space.

The method proposed in alternative (d) is described as follows:

(1) Use skidded, corrugated steel, storage boxes for storing and handling both dross and concentrates. The boxes are cubes 4 feet on a side . . . hold 3000 pounds of dross or 4000 pounds of concentrate . . . can be stacked two high.
(2) Provide 60 boxes for dross . . . store 180,000 pounds or 3 carloads.
(3) Provide 80 boxes for concentrates . . . store 320,000 pounds . . . corresponds to one month supply at rated capacity.
(4) Provide sufficient preparation capacity to process at least 60 tons (2 carloads) in a normal 8 hour shift. An occasional peak (90 tons per day) may require a 12 hour operation.
(5) Sample each lot by weighing the concentrate and analyzing an appropriate sample . . . . The accuracy in estimating net metallic content is . . . good.

(C) *Receiving and Shipping Facilities.* Three alternative methods . . . are compared in Work Sheet No. 2. These comprise:

(a) Spur track at grade level with dock elevated to car floor height.
(b) Spur track depressed to grade . . . car floor level with ground.
(c) Same as (b) but long enough to accommodate simultaneous loading and unloading.

The analysis indicates (c) as the most favorable . . . . Entry and exit tracks require about 100 feet each at 4 percent grade, . . . total of 300 feet of spur track.

(D) *Crushing and Grinding Operations.*

(1) Selection of Crushing Equipment (Work Sheet No. 3). Among standard crushing equipment the jaw-crusher seems best adapted for the initial size reduction. A 24 x 30 inch machine, single or double toggle, powered with a 60 horsepower motor is required. The throughput to 1 inch and under will be about 20 tons per hour . . . although in excess of the required 8 to 10 tons per hour . . . the size is dictated by the larger chunks in the feed.
(2) Feed to the Crusher. A jaw-crusher is self-feeding. A hopper, large enough to contain the contents of two boxes and opening directly into

the crusher, is convenient. Five or six loaded boxes . . . placed on a slightly inclined roller conveyor . . . roll down to an appropriate elevating and tilting mechanism under the control of the crusher operator.

(3) Delivery to the Rod Mill Feed Hopper. The crusher is elevated above floor level admitting a belt conveyor with magnetic pulley . . . to separate ferritic materials. The belt, inclined at 18 degrees, . . . elevates the material 9 feet in a horizontal run of 27.5 feet . . . to a 100 cubic foot rod mill feed hopper.

(4) First Screening. The rod mill feed hopper . . . delivers to a 3 x 8 foot, 14 mesh vibratory screen . . . separates coarse materials from nonmetallic fines. The coarse material feeds into the rod mill . . . waste is carried away by a belt conveyor.

(5) Rod Mill. Crushing and grinding in the rod mill separates non-metallic material from aluminum. The cascading action of charged material and heavy rods . . . as the mill turns . . . disintegrates the aluminum agglomerates . . . rubs off adhering nonmetallic material. A 4 x 8 foot rod mill with a 14000 pound charge of bars running at 30 rpm. . . . 40 horsepower . . . has a throughput of 7.5 to 8 tons per hour. The nonmetallics reduce to 8 mesh and finer.

(6) Final Screening Operation. The exit material from the rod mill is received on a double deck vibratory screen. Material not passing the first deck is recycled . . . material passing through the first screen but not the second is . . . concentrate, fines passing through the second is discharged to the conveyor belt. The concentrate moves on a belt over a magnetic pulley and is discharged into a storage box.

(7) Handling of Finished Concentrate. A slightly inclined roller conveyor receives 4 or 5 empty boxes, the end one receiving the finished concentrate from the discharge belt. The end section . . . on a weighing scale . . . at 4000 pounds the scale trips a stop, . . . full box rolls out of the way . . . empty one takes its place. Fork lift truck removes full boxes when convenient and sets them in the concentrate storage area . . . and replaces empties on the conveyor.

(E) *Waste Disposal.* The easiest way to carry off waste . . . is by conveyor belt. Fines from first and second screening operations are discharged on individual conveyor belts. These discharge on the main disposal conveyor belt. A section of semi-portable conveyor, properly inclined, dumps the days production on the mound or in the pit . . . spread out with a bulldozer later.

(F) *Melting Facilities.* At rated capacity the furnace must have a throughput of 2000 pounds per hour to keep pace on a one-shift basis. The furnace must be designed to melt 3000 pounds per hour. The preliminary design (Work Sheet No. 4) specifies the following:

(1) Consumption of natural gas is 4500 cubic feet per hour.

(2) Holding capacity of the furnace (metal 18 inches deep) is 25,000 pounds. This includes the puddling well.

(3) Combustion chamber between the surface of the metal bath and the roof is 3 feet . . . the horizontal dimensions are 9 feet wide by 10 feet long.

(4) Puddling well has inside dimensions of $2\frac{1}{2}$ feet by 9 feet by 18 inches deep.

(5) Bath temperature at designed rate of operation is 1320°F.

(6) Temperature drop in the puddling well at designed rate of operation is 50°F.

(G) *Casting Machine.* The capacity of the casting machine is set at 3000 pounds per hour . . . permitting the day's production to be cast in 5 hours. The specifications of the ingot shape and the machine are given below (Work sheet No. 5).

(1) The ingots are 21 pounds . . . the ends are cut away for ease of handling when packaged. A stack of ingots . . . 6 wide and 8 high are strapped together forming a package of 1000 pounds.

(2) Ingot molds are of cast iron . . . one-inch wall thickness . . . weight is 100 pounds.

(3) In steady-state operation an ingot mold cools to 250°F. and rises to 700°F.

(4) The mold conveyor carries 116 molds. The pouring rate is 144 ingots per hour. The turn around time for a mold is 0.8 hours.

(5) The pouring station is 29 molds upstream from the dumping point.

(6) Cooling sprays will be required on the molds . . . 315 gallons per hour accomplishes the cooling . . . 29 gallons per hour are lost by evaporation.

(7) The casting machine is 21 feet center to center of the sprockets and 24 feet overall in length.

Comments: In this section the preliminary design concept is set forth. The back up for the design is contained in the work sheets which are not included here because of their necessary length and detail. In the section following, the specifications are made more specific and costs are estimated. The costs will be necessary in order to prepare a budget and to test the financial feasibility of the project.

5. THE PLANT—MAJOR EQUIPMENT, COST AND LAYOUT

(A) *Storage Facilities:*
Heavy duty, corrugated steel, selfskidded storage boxes, 4 × 4 × 4 ft at $150 each...... $22,500

(B) *Spur Tracks and Docks:*
Dock pavement and retaining walls.......... $4,200
Spur track, 300 ft.......................   6,000
Car spotter.............................   2,500   12,700

(C) *Jaw Crusher (Installed):*
Size 24 × 30 in. with 60 hp motor..........   13,200

(D) *Rod Mill* (*Installed*):
Size 4 × 8 ft. with 40 hp motor   18,500

(E) *Vibratory Screens:*
Primary screen, single deck 3 × 8 ft $2,200
Secondary screen, double deck 3 × 8 ft   2,800   4,000

(F) *Conveyors, Hoppers, and Magnetic Pulleys:*
Belt conveyors, 24 in. × 50 ft $2,500
Hoppers, two of 4 cu. yd. each   2,000
Magnetic pulleys and rectifiers (2)   2,000
Feeder for rod mill   7,500   14,000

(G) *Special Conveying and Elevating Equipment:*
Roller conveyors and elevators (2)   7,500

(H) *Waste Material Conveyors:*
Belt conveyors, 18 in. × 200 ft   5,000

(I) *Melting Furnace:*
Cost of furnace   15,000

(J) *Furnace Feeder:*
Special conveyor and elevating device $7,500
Platform scale, 6000 lb   800   8,300

(K) *Casting Machine:*
Molds, 150 each $15 . . . . $2,250
Conveyor frame, chains, sprockets   5,000
Reduction gear and motor   1,000
Pouring device   1,000
Miscellaneous   750   10,000

(L) *Material Handling Equipment:*
Power scoop ($\frac{1}{4}$ yd) $3,000
Two ton fork lift truck   3,000
Bulldozer tractor (used)   3,000
Five yard dump truck (used)   7,000   16,000

(M) *Chemical Laboratory:*
Equipment and furniture   2,000

(N) *Dust Collectors and Hoods:*
Multiple cyclone, 20,000 cfm $2,500
Blower and motor   2,000
Hoods and ducts   3,500   8,000

(O) *Buildings and Pavements:*
Buildings, steel frame, corrugated metal, con-
crete floor—9600 sq. ft $48,000
Pavement, 10,000 sq. ft   7,500
Office and laboratory—1000 sq. ft   10,000
Electric power installation 200 KVA   6,000   71,500

Total Fixed Investment $228,000

6. WORK FORCE AT RATED CAPACITY

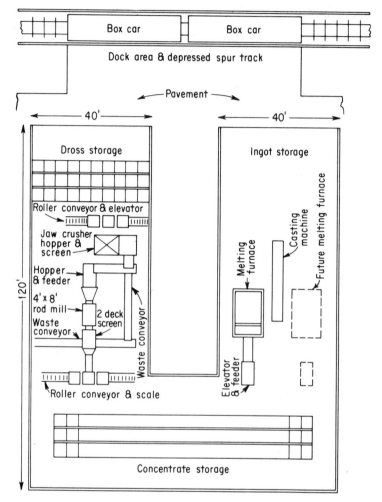

FIGURE 12.1

The following work force is required:

Number	Job Description	Monthly Cost
2	Operators—power scoop, bulldozer and fork lift truck at $2.50 per hour.............................	$840
3	Furnace operators at $2.50 per hr....................	1,260
3	Semi skilled laborers at $1.90 per hr.................	980
1	Clerk—receiving, shipping and ingot bundling at $2.50 per hr...	420
1	Maintenance mechanic at $2.75 per hr................	460
1	Chemist at $2.75 per hr..............................	460
1	Office clerk at $2.50 per hr..........................	420

Number	Job Description	Monthly Cost
1	Truck driver at $2.50 per hr............................	420
1	Foreman...	550
	Net payroll (not including payroll expense)..................	$5,810

7. COST OF MANUFACTURE

(A) *Sources and Cost of Raw Material:*
  (1) Primary sources (20 to 22% Al)
    Estimated available 425 tons at $36.......... $15,300
  (2) Secondary sources (10 to 12% Al)
    Estimated available 500 tons at $20..........   10,000
  (3) Foundries serviced by truck (20 to 22% Al)
    Estimated available 100 tons at $20.......... $2,000
  (4) Cost of freight in by rail at $4.10 per ton......   3,800
  (5) Estimated recovery is 150 tons of Al.

(B) *Cost of Manufacturing:*
  (1) Raw materials consumed—
    Average monthly purchase.................. $27,300
    Add freight inward........................   3,800

    Cost of raw material......................   31,100
  (2) Direct labor—
    At scheduled pay rates..................... $3,700
    Add payroll expenses (20%)................   700

    Cost of direct labor......................   4,400
  (3) Manufacturing Expenses (Work sheet No. 6)—
    Indirect labor............................ $2,300
    Payroll expense...........................   500
    Factory supplies..........................   1,100
    Provision for depreciation.................   1,800
    Utilities and fuel.........................   1,400
    Repairs..................................   600
    Property taxes............................   200
    Miscellaneous............................   200

    Total manufacturing expenses..............   8,100
    Cost of goods sold........................   43,600

(C) *Projected Profit or Loss*
  (1) Gross sales at rated capacity................   60,000
  (2) Cost of goods sold..........................   43,600
  (3) Selling and general expense
    Salesman, buying and selling............... $600
    Travelling expense........................   400
    Telephone and telegraph...................   300

    Total selling and general expense............   1,300

(4) Expected profit before taxes and interest on
     loans 15,100

(D) *Variable and Non Variable Costs*

  (1) Non variable costs

Selling costs and general expense	$1,300	
Supervision and clerical	1,700	
Provision for depreciation	1,800	
Property taxes and miscellaneous	400	
Non variable costs		5,200

  (2) Variable costs at rated capacity

Cost of goods sold	$43,600	
Non variable costs (subtract)	5,200	
Variable costs		38,400

  (3) Variable costs at half capacity

Raw materials	$13,700	
Freight inward	1,900	
Direct labor and payroll expense	3,300	
Factory supplies	600	
Utilities and fuel	1,000	
Repairs	400	
Variable costs		21,000

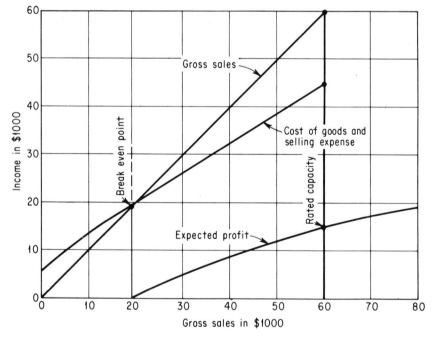

FIG. 12.2 Operating Characteristics of Aluminum Recovery Plant.

(E) *Break Even Point*: See the accompanying chart. The break-even is at
$\frac{1}{3}$ of rated capacity, namely at a production of 50 tons per month and
gross sales of $20,000.

134

Comments: A continuous processing plant can frequently be reduced to a set of subsystems in series such that the output of one is the input to the next one. The interactions among the subsystems is reduced to the simplest level, the major issue being compatibility in the input-output relations between successive subsystems. In the present case the system reduces to two subsystems, namely receiving and processing dross to concentrate in the first, and melting, casting, and shipping pig aluminum in the second subsystem. With an implied upper limit on the capital investment and fixed specifications on the product, profit is maximized by minimizing a properly weighted combination of labor and storage time in each of the subsystems. These problems were considered in some of the work sheets of the original report.

As an example the archetype of the first subsystem includes an idealized storage for dross, a processor for converting dross to concentrate, and an idealized storage for concentrate. If the dross storage is made large, the processor and the concentrate storage can be small. If the dross storage is small, the processor and the concentrate storage must be larger. With each of these subsubsystems we associate costs of capital investment, labor, inventory, and losses due to oxidation. With these costs set up functionally we have a mathematical archetype in which the design parameters can be adjusted to best advantage in relation to the minimization of the criterion of operating costs.